Beyond the Therapeutic Community

Beyond the Therapeutic Community

Social Learning and Social Psychiatry

by Maxwell Jones

New Haven and London, Yale University Press

To my wife, Kerstin

Contents

Introduction

This book is meant to complement my two earlier books,[1] which were essentially descriptive accounts of a therapeutic community. There is a gap of ten years between those two publications. Now, after thirty years' experience in community treatment, I believe it appropriate to attempt a theoretical formulation of some of the concepts used in therapeutic community practice. I am only too aware that such an attempt may serve little purpose other than to draw attention to the large gaps in our knowledge about using social forces in the environment to complement the treatment methods of psychiatry. However, the rapid growth of social and community psychiatry makes it imperative that we examine critically our practice in this field. The critics of social psychiatry can fairly state that the rapid growth of community psychiatry has far outstripped our knowledge. This alone would justify

1. Maxwell Jones, *Social Psychiatry* (London, Tavistock Publications, 1952); published in the U.S.A. as *The Therapeutic Community* (New York, Basic Books, 1953); *Social Psychiatry in the Community, in Hospitals, and in Prisons* (Springfield, Ill., Chas. C. Thomas, 1962).

an attempt to examine what one is doing and why; theoretical
formulations are a prelude to more exact studies, and they
may anticipate future attempts at validation.[2] Many of our
basic principles are still too vague to lend themselves to
exact studies by the behavioral sciences or any other research
approach. There is nothing new in all this; one could cite
the example of education, which goes merrily along, at
times with staggering pomposity, despite the fact that as
yet surprisingly little is known about the processes of learning.

Painful communication in a therapeutic community is one
of the major themes of this book. In a very real sense "all the
world's a stage," and our upbringing, in the home, at school,
and in society generally, prepares us for our role as actors.
As a corollary to this one can say that we tend to live by a
double standard; we may be playing two quite different and
often contradictory roles in our official and private worlds.
All this is familiar to the point of being banal, and it might
be wise to let well alone, were it not for the fact that all
the evidence relating to the development of mental illness
points to the need to examine this dichotomy. People need
people—not just for company, but for support, understanding, and enlightenment. At times of stress, what one needs
most to communicate is often invested with feelings of shame,
guilt, and fear. It goes without saying that there are many
parents, teachers, ministers, and other individuals in positions
of responsibility who, as part of their function as human

2. Robert Rapoport and his research associates made a heroic
effort to validate some of our earlier theoretical formulations in a
therapeutic community. See his *Community as Doctor* (London,
Tavistock Publications, 1960).

beings, listen dispassionately to painful communication. But kindness is often not enough, particularly in the face of impending or actual psychiatric illness. In these circumstances such skills as we have in the medical and helping services must be applied as effectively and economically as possible. In view of the shortages of trained personnel, full use should be made of ancillary help. The concept of the therapeutic community draws attention to the need to make the optimal use of the potential in trained staff, volunteers, patients, their relatives, and any other people with a contribution to make to the betterment of mental health.

It is difficult to understand why in the past psychiatry has been content to imitate the principles and practices of general medicine. As an example, psychiatric hospitals have much of the formal hierarchical structure of general hospitals, and relatively little attention has been given to their entirely different function. To begin with it is difficult to understand why one should talk about psychiatric hospitals at all. Goffman[3] has drawn attention to many of the absurdities of the practice of psychiatry in large institutions. In this context it is doubtful if the much-heralded small psychiatric units in general hospitals can easily get away from the dominant influence of the larger parent hospital in order to develop a therapeutic culture appropriate to the task of helping psychiatric patients.[4]

3. Erving Goffman, *Asylums: Essays on the Social Situation of Mental Patients and other Inmates* (New York, Doubleday, 1961).

4. Maxwell Jones and Joy Tuxford, "Some Common Trends in British and American Mental Hospital Psychiatry," *Lancet, 1* (1963), 433–35.

This book attempts to look at the problems of the mentally ill, or those in danger of becoming so, from the point of view of the patient, or potential patient, rather than from the more traditional doctor-centered frame of reference. This sounds very grand and, in fact, nothing very new is said. But the emphasis certainly differs from that in the current practice of psychiatry. The main thesis of this book is that one must add to the familiar psychiatric treatment methods, both psychological and physical, the relatively neglected social and environmental dimensions.

In trying to support the optimal use of forces in the social environment in treatment and prevention of mental illness, I am struck by the lack of attention paid to social organization both within the psychiatric institutions and within the community. It is easier to talk about social structure within a psychiatric hospital than in the community, because of its size. The psychiatric hospital can be seen as a microcosm of society outside, and its social structure and culture can be changed with relative ease, compared to the world outside. For this reason "therapeutic communities" to date have been largely confined to psychiatric institutions. They represent a useful pilot run preliminary to the much more difficult task of trying to establish a therapeutic community for psychiatric purposes in society at large. It seems reasonable to suppose that at the present time a therapeutic community represents the best setting in which training for community psychiatry can be carried out. It is for this reason that most of the material in this book is based on experience of therapeutic communities in hospitals during the past thirty years.

Chapters 1 to 4 describe and examine many of the concepts that have evolved from therapeutic community practice in hospitals. Chapter 5 has been the most difficult to write, because our experience in applying such principles to community practice has been much shorter. Most of the principles described in the first four chapters are relevant to the practice of psychiatry in the outside community, but modifications will be necessary when these principles are applied to community psychiatry.

Chapter 1 is concerned with certain aspects of social organization. How can one begin to structure the environment of the hospital to facilitate treatment? In my experience there are three major objectives: the establishment of two-way communication involving as far as possible all personnel, both patients and staff; decision-making machinery at all levels, so that everyone has the feeling that he is identified with the aims of the hospital, with change, and with its successes and failures; the development of a therapeutic culture reflecting the attitudes and beliefs of patients and staff and highlighting the importance of roles and role relationships. The ideal circumstances for the development of a therapeutic community include the establishment of a new hospital without long-standing traditions, where one can choose a staff oriented toward therapeutic community practice. It is, however, a slow but rewarding task to try to bring about change within an established institution.

An attempt has been made in Chapter 1 to capture the dynamic processes resulting from a flexible social organization. In this context we have discussed change and evolution as byproducts of social structure. As far as I know, none of the disciplines that converge on psychiatry offer any real training in the principles of social organization.

It is our conviction that the setting in which treatment

occurs is extremely important. At times it may determine whether or not a particular treatment method (psychological or physical) is effective. So far hospitals and community treatment programs have paid remarkably little attention to this significant aspect of treatment, and the therapeutic community approach represents an attempt to correct this state of affairs.

Leadership is discussed in Chapter 2. The importance of the leader in any treatment program is obvious; but equally obvious is the haphazard way in which leadership emerges in the traditional psychiatric hospital. A consultant psychiatrist, whose whole experience is in the clinical field, may overnight become a physician superintendent and be expected to play a role significantly different from the one for which he has been trained, although he may have administrative experience in his own wards or as a substitute for an absent administrator. There is a trend to make medical administrators increasingly clinically involved. Clark[5] has drawn attention to the possibilities of the administrator as therapist. In the United States several courses in medical administration have been developed in recent years, and this has done something to correct the lack of training for an administrative leadership role. In a therapeutic community, an attempt is made to examine both the factors involved in leadership and the different types of leadership which should be allowed to emerge. In particular the role relationship between the formal leader and his deputy has enormous importance and may affect the social climate of the entire hospital. Leadership must be considered in relation to the social structure as

5. David H. Clark, *Administrative Therapy* (London, Tavistock Publications, 1964).

a whole; the authority structure of a hospital is best separated from the concept of leadership. In a therapeutic community, authority is delegated in large measure to a group of people involved in any one particular area, e.g. a ward or a department.

In my own case as physician superintendent, I practically never make a unilateral decision, and the same applies to the two other major authority figures, the hospital secretary and the principal nursing officer. We invariably discuss important matters in the appropriate committee or subgroup and try as far as possible to achieve decision by consensus. This type of leadership on the part of authority figures blends almost imperceptibly with "functional leadership," which emerges in response to a particular situation. If the senior staff committee, with the three formal leaders present, along with other doctors and department heads, were discussing the question of the establishment of a hostel or half-way house, leadership for such a project would probably emerge in the discussion and would be agreed to by explicit or implicit consensus.

Even in clinical psychiatry there is no reason why leadership should be on the basis of the formalized authority structure and status system of the National Health Service, in Great Britain, or the more informal structures in the United States. As an example, in a particular ward or unit the establishment of evening family groups for therapeutic purposes might be seen as best carried out by the psychologist, social worker, or nurse rather than by the psychiatrist—by the person with the most suitable personality and group skills. This has happened at Fort Logan Mental Health Center, in Denver, Colorado, where leadership of a treatment team has at times been assigned to a psychologist with the doctor seeing to the medical needs of the patients.

Patient leadership is perhaps the most neglected aspect of this subject. In psychiatric hospitals there is a natural disinclination to hand over much responsibility and authority to patients, and this is reinforced by a passive dependency characteristic of all groups of psychiatric patients. It is all too easy to reconcile this passive-dependent attitude with the cultural image of the doctor–patient relationship and with the expectations of a patient in any doctor's office. Moreover, most patients in hospital have failed to meet the expectations of the community in which they live and are in general only too pleased to be led and have something "done for them" by the doctor and staff. Much can be done by the introduction of therapeutic groups to help patients play a significant part in the treatment of themselves and other patients. One can, however, go far beyond this stage and create responsible leadership roles for patients within the hospital community. Such a functional role in the life of the hospital does much to change the image of the patient in his own mind and in the minds of his peers. This is seen as a good preparation for his return to society.

Multiple leadership is probably the most important aspect of leadership, and it is here that there is the greatest need for change. The hierarchical social structure of institutions, whether medical, industrial, or political, invests the leadership role with enormous power. There is probably an element of truth in the common statement that power corrupts. There is nothing wrong with authority as such, but its abuse leads to frustration and incompetence in organizations. Multiple leadership means the distribution of authority and power to

many people, and even more important, to people who communicate freely in groups. This brings us to the fascinating
concept of group leadership, which may well become increasingly important as therapeutic community principles are
developed. Such a concept seems compatible with the ideal
of making the optimal use of the potential within any one
functional group or organization.

The principles of multiple or group leadership are difficult
to apply to hospital practice and infinitely more difficult to
apply to the community. Nevertheless, if community psychiatry is to succeed, and the various disciplines involved
in national health programs are to function optimally, then
multiple leadership must be made to function in practice.
As an example, leadership in community psychiatry need not
necessarily be in the hands of the medical officer of health,
the psychiatric consultant, or the psychiatric social worker.
Each has his own particular area of competence, and how far
his area can achieve its full usefulness will depend on the
capacity of the leader to utilize the skills of the allied services and bring about one unified community service with
multiple leadership. At the moment such integration of
services is left largely to chance and the good will of the
personnel concerned. We believe that far more attention
should be paid to the principles and practice of leadership
in the training of personnel in the psychiatric and social work
fields. Various inquiries are going on at present in Great
Britain concerning the structure of local authorities and the
future of social work organizations. Everywhere one sees
signs of the unwillingness on the part of any one discipline
to give up any of its authority, and even within a single discipline like social work, despite active attempts at professional

integration, the various subgroups in practice show little enthusiasm to relinquish any of their existing power.

One of the most controversial aspects of a therapeutic community is decision-making by consensus. This is one of the topics discussed in Chapter 3. It is used in the relative rather than the absolute sense and at the very least indicates that the people who may be affected by any decision should be given the opportunity to participate in the decision-making process. To achieve complete agreement on any difficult administrative decision is impossible. The aim of the democratic decision-making process is to have at least the majority of people identified with the project. The people who put a decision into practice will have more interest and enjoyment in it if they feel identified with the project from the start.

Members of committees and informal groups that form around administrative and therapeutic problems often realize that what is being discussed bears little relationship to the underlying feelings in the meeting. Even in formal committees little is to be gained by slavishly following an agenda when everyone knows that strong feelings are being aroused that cannot be expressed. It would seem better, whenever possible, to forego any hope of dealing with the formal agenda until such time as the "hidden agenda" can be explored and understood. Only in this way can the principle of group identification with a project be put into practice. Other matters discussed in Chapter 3 include the concepts of feedback, rumor, and sanctions as they apply to a therapeutic community.

Social learning as described in Chapter 4 is one of the fundamental concepts of therapeutic community practice.

Our use of the term "social learning" will please no one, but we need to express the concept of learning as a social process —as opposed to the more behaviorist theories of learning on the one hand and the psychoanalytic concept of insight on the other. It seems logical to separate teaching altogether from learning, although the two are of course complementary. Teaching is seen as a one-way communication from teacher to pupil, for the purpose of absorbing and memorizing facts and accumulating knowledge. How such a process of one-way communication can initiate thought and explore the new combinations and permutations made possible by new awareness is an open question.

In Chapter 4 no attempt is made to consider the vast field of learning. Our concern is with social interaction in a secure setting, which encourages the expression of feeling, and with resource personnel present to use the situation for the furtherance of learning. This process is seen as an end-product of all the factors that have already been touched on in the previous discussion. The social structure must be of such a kind as to enhance communication and diminish status differentiation, so that something of a peer group emerges. The free expression of feeling cannot occur unless the social structure is such that sanctions are positive and reprisals are virtually impossible. Such a formal social organization is not enough. Staff must be trained over a long period (at least a year) so that they are sufficiently secure themselves to be able to tolerate the free communication of feeling. Nor is participation in therapeutic groups enough; the staff should, as far as possible, have experience of sensitivity (or T-Group) training, so that they become aware of themselves as other people see them. This falls far short of a personal psychoanalytic training but gives some of its advantages to staff members.

Perhaps the greatest difficulty in this type of training applies to the most senior levels of staff. Matrons, physician superintendents, and others have usually been trained in an era when experience in group work was almost unknown. For such senior staff personnel to forego the protection of their rank presents difficulties. To have a senior staff member accept discussion and criticism of his performance in a clinical or administrative situation by other staff members, and even patients, is difficult without a training period. Nevertheless, this is the aim lest all the principles inherent in the concept of a therapeutic community be negated by negative sanctions and the abuse of authority from the formal leader.

Social learning need not be limited to formal situations, such as therapeutic or training groups, but can probably apply effectively to specific situations as they arise. There seems to be good reason for thinking that learning occurs more readily when people's emotions are involved. It is for this reason that we utilize crisis situations both for training and to resolve the crisis itself. In brief we feel that training of doctors, social workers, psychologists, nurses, occupational therapists, and so on should be carried out in the course of the daily routine. Situations which result in interpersonal difficulties can readily be turned into "living-learning situations," provided the personnel have the motivation and the staff have the skill to lead to social learning.

In the long run, the capacity to utilize social learning depends on our early upbringing and the influence of teachers and other responsible leaders, in short, on individual personality development. How far the concept of social learning can be applied to education is still an open question. Nevertheless, the indications are that something like a revolution in education may be anticipated in the near future. Signs of change are particularly apparent in the elementary schools, where much more attention is paid to social interaction and social learning than is apparent in higher education. In the latter the examination system precludes any kind of social interaction that might otherwise occur. It is tempting to speculate about the future of teaching and learning if they are given their proper emphasis and complement each other to a greater extent than at present. In such a brave new world averagely intelligent individuals may more easily see points of view other than their own and feel less threatened by new ideas. Such a change in our social values, willingness to learn, and capacity to form group identifications seem to offer possibilities for the future which are every bit as exciting as developments in the scientific world.

Chapter 5 attempts to anticipate future developments in community psychiatry; as yet, very little is known about it. Inevitably the development of the therapeutic community in the community presents far greater problems than in a hospital. Nevertheless, the importance of the peer group, the development of the therapeutic culture, attitudes to mental illness, communication, and a democratic egalitarian structure all seem to have as much relevance in the community as in the hospital. It remains to be seen how far multiple leadership in a multidisciplinary setting and the integration of services required to bring about satisfactory community psychiatry can be achieved. Community psychiatry offers an immensely exciting challenge for the future. But much will depend on the training that people in psychiatry and the allied disciplines receive. Hopefully, training can do something to offset the abuse of authority, the struggle for power, and the isolated position that is adopted by many disciplines when coordination and integration are called for. However, the mere existence of the field of community psychiatry suggests tremendous changes in the attitudes adopted by the relevant professional groups and by the community at large.

The final chapter (Chapter 6) looks at possible future developments in psychiatry. The impact of the computer age is already apparent, and technology is no longer totally subservient to the needs of the individual. In the past the history of psychiatry was basically determined by the personality and abilities of the leaders. In the future the psychiatrist will be less important as an individual, and his survival in social psychiatry will depend on his capacity to find a role compatible with the needs of society and the demands of the computer age. This concept of functional usefulness in collaboration with other disciplines and with the community at large has to be reconciled with the new areas of specialization created by technology. The machine and its handmaiden, the social organization, have come to stay.

Chapter 1. Social Structure, Change, and Evolution

The practice of psychiatry calls for certain skills, not only in relation to the psychiatrist, but also in allied disciplines such as nursing, psychology, social work, occupational therapy and so on. Behavioral scientists are coming to play an increasingly important part in psychiatry; but apart from a few research appointments, few if any psychiatric hospitals have a behavioral scientist in their formal establishment. Moreover, the psychiatrist during his training is unlikely to have had much contact with behavioral science, in theory or in practice. This gap in the integration of medical, psychiatric, and behavioral science practice needs to be corrected in psychiatric hospitals and the practice of psychiatry in the outside community. Within the psychiatric hospital the concept of the therapeutic community has evolved as an attempt to bring about this integration of psychiatry and the behavioral sciences. The social structure of a psychiatric hospital seems to me to be the most neglected field in the practice of present-day psychiatry. The skills of a well-trained and competent psychiatrist may be largely negated if the social

environment in which treatment is carried out is unsatisfactory. The aim of the therapeutic community is to help
patients by making the optimal use of the skills and potential
of staff, patients, and their relatives. Thus to the treatment
skills of the staff—in both psychological and physical dimensions—is added the use of the social environment in further-
ing treatment. Group psychotherapy, by creating an artificial
social environment in which interaction between patients
and staff can occur, is a start in this direction. However, it is
concerned more with the application of psychoanalytic principles to individuals interacting in a formal group session
than with problems of how the social environment of the
hospital and the outside community can be modified or
restructured to reinforce formal treatment methods. Whether such social developments will in time come to represent a
new dimension in treatment remains an open question. Pro-
vocative new horizons are emerging, such as the concept of
primary prevention as described by Caplan,[1] the theory and
practice of environmental therapy as described by the Cum-
mings,[2] and the use of the hospital community to bring about
attitude change and "learning," as described by myself.[3]

In this chapter I consider social structure under three
headings: communication, decision-making, and therapeutic
culture. I attempt to show how these three factors have
changed during my years at Dingleton Hospital, a 400-bed
in-patient hospital, in Melrose, Scotland (starting in Decem-

1. G. Caplan, *Principles of Preventive Psychiatry* (London,
Tavistock Publications, 1964).
2. J. Cumming and E. Cumming, *Ego and Milieu* (New York,
Atherton Press, 1962).
3. Maxwell Jones, *Social Psychiatry in Practice* (London, Pen-
guin Books), in Press.

ber 1962). My past experience had impressed me with the importance of the social structure of a hospital and its effect on the hospital community. I deliberately set out to try to bring about an open communication system, decision-making machinery, and—as a result of these two factors—a change in the cohesiveness, attitudes, and beliefs of the patient and staff population as a whole. To try to capture something of the dynamic processes resulting from these modifications in social structure, I shall consider two further topics, under the headings of change and evolution.

Communication

In hospitals communication from above, down to the various professional groups and to patients, may be relatively efficient, but the opposite is seldom true. The only psychiatric social worker on the staff when I arrived at Dingleton told me that the doctors made relatively little use of her. She complained that her office was in an extremely isolated part of the hospital, where people seldom visited her. Such communication blocks are not uncommon in psychiatric hospitals; such lack of communication is well recognized by the staff, who themselves are the sufferers. But nobody knows how to correct such a problem, particularly if blocks in communication at least in part represent a defense of key people in the face of threats to their own security, prestige, or power. To open up communication would in many cases entail painful confrontation and exposure to situations with which the individuals feel unable to cope. Communication blocks occur for perfectly good reasons; they are not due to wickedness on the part of particular individuals. To open up communications under such circumstances calls for skills in group dynamics and applied sociology which, as yet, are rare in the senior staff of present-day hospitals.

A newcomer in a position of authority may have a honeymoon period when, because of his fresh viewpoint, he may act as a catalyst. His interpretation of his role and the role relationships he forms will be watched carefully by his colleagues. Acting on the temptation to form special relationships and communication channels can easily lead to feelings of rejection and resentment by other senior staff members, and the development of splits and cliques within the senior staff group. The honeymoon period ends all too soon, unless the new arrival can convince his colleagues of the necessity to establish formal communication channels at all levels, so that two-way communication may develop.

Having had considerable experience in developing therapeutic communities, and as the physician superintendent, I could ensure that the development of a rational social organization was given positive sanctions and a high priority. It was particularly fortunate that the hospital secretary and the board of management he served were extremely cooperative and did everything in their power to support me. Moreover the hospital, thanks to my predecessor and the senior doctors, had already reached the point where a change to the therapeutic community was desired; only the know-how was lacking. This motivation toward change by some of the senior personnel was an enormous advantage and considerably enhanced my role as catalyst, apart altogether from my technical skills. Soon after I took office, I noted that the schism between doctors and the matron and her deputy was the most important single problem. Communication between these two services was at a very low level. This was partly due to the fact that my predecessor did not hold regular staff meetings. In fact the conference room next to my office seemed to be almost completely unused.

After three weeks we had started to try to improve the situation by initiating biweekly senior staff meetings where the matron, deputy matron, and assistant matrons met with the four doctors, the psychiatric social worker, the occupational therapist, and my secretary. The matron attended one group therapy session with me and seemed to be quite interested. She agreed to the establishment of a monthly meeting of all nursing staff available, and the doctors. At this stage I was becoming even more aware of the lack of an open communication system.

The result was a kind of cell-like quality to the whole hospital, where there were few links among the various activities and departments. At the first meeting of the work therapy subcommittee, the hospital secretary, the psychiatric social worker, two of the doctors, some of the senior nursing staff, the occupational therapist, the rehabilitation officer, and the supervisors from the laundry, garden, kitchen, and dining room were present. Its goal was to make recommendations to the senior staff committee and bring about an integration of all the activity programs. This subcommittee has met weekly ever since. By the end of six weeks, the nursing subcommittee had met and discussed the general topic of mixed sexes on the wards in relation to both patients and staff. It was proposed that two male staff nurses be moved to the female side and that these should be volunteers in the first instance. This was a prelude to a much greater mixing of the sexes, both staff and patients, on the wards.

At this time we had also had the first meeting of our Journal Club. Between fifty and sixty staff turned up and discussed Denis Martin's book about a therapeutic community, entitled *Adventure in Psychiatry*. In the discussion following the presentation, I mentioned the first meeting we had had that day in one of the female long-stay wards. Only about half the patients chose to participate. They raised some important issues, including the different rates of pay they received for work done. They were unable to understand the principle on which they were paid and why some people got more than others: they also mentioned bed-making, and on asking them to develop this theme it became clear that they were puzzled as to why beds were made mainly by themselves in the morning and then remade by the nurses at night. I commented that it seemed difficult to know who were patients and who were staff in such a curious mix-up, and was delighted to see that the matron laughed heartily at this comment, although presumably it was she who had made this stipulation about the night nurses remaking the beds.

Communications were developing rapidly in other wards. When I arrived, my two senior psychiatric colleagues both had ward meetings in their respective admission wards, and although these were the only two ward meetings in the hospital at that time, they epitomized the latent potential to develop communications and group treatment, which was already present in many of the staff. Eager to develop ward meetings and group therapy, they welcomed me to the already existing treatment groups. I was amazed to learn at this time that nurses did not have access to the patients' notes; that the admissions procedure was a formal interview between doctor and patient; and that the amount of feedback to the nursing staff was left largely to chance.

I soon was able to interview my first two new patients with several staff members present. This seemed to cause no embarrassment whatsoever to the new admission and the relative. We instituted a weekly doctors' meeting to discuss purely medical problems and also administrative matters such as annual leave.

By the end of six weeks I was beginning to feel quite optimistic about improved communications. The numerous meetings we established in the hospital were tending to bud off, so that subcommittees were developing and the groups are spreading to other wards. The communication network appeared to link up satisfactorily with the Hospital Board of Management. They were well aware of the fact that the recommendations made to them had been discussed in the senior staff committee, if not in other subcommittees, so that they were getting not only my point of view but the point of view of the senior staff generally.

Since these early weeks, communications have, I think, steadily improved, and during the last year we have been paying more and more attention to our communications with the outside community. At the present time, there are over 100 groups held weekly at Dingleton, which means that in any one week-day there are more than 20 groups. These are divided into:

Administrative Groups A daily meeting of the hospital secretary, principal nursing officer, and physician superintendent (the "Holy Trinity") takes place for half an hour, as well as a daily meeting of the senior staff committee, about sixteen members in all, comprising all senior trained staff, which lasts forty-five minutes. These two groups deal with all the administrative problems of the day, as well as problems bearing on patient management. All major problems are referred ultimately to the senior staff committee for decision and approval, as described on the next section on decision-making. In this way we avoid unilateral decisions and aim as far as possible at decision by consensus. Other administrative groups include weekly meetings of the charge nurses and ward sisters, the social work department, work therapy department, the education committee, entertainments committee, and so on.

Treatment Groups   These vary from daily ward meetings and therapeutic groups for patients who are considered suitable for this type of verbal interaction; to activity groups for long-stay and geriatric patients, who are more appropriately engaged on group tasks rather than verbal discussion; to nonverbal groups of the very simplest kind, such as music and movement and pastimes such as painting and card games, for the most regressed patients. All these groups are followed by a review for approximately half an hour when the staff discusses what happened during the treatment session. This group approach to treatment is discussed fully elsewhere.[4]

Training Groups   All therapeutic groups are followed by a review attended by all staff. This forms an important training opportunity, because the various disciplines involved— medical, nursing, social work, and so on—are in a position to discuss their differing perceptions of what happened in the treatment group and also to examine their own role

4. Maxwell Jones, *Social Psychiatry in Practice.*

relationships. There are in addition staff seminars for training in group psychotherapy, which take the form of sensitivity training, or T-Group training.

Work Groups   As far as possible, all patients are involved in productive work for pay. These work groups are supervised by work therapists, and more emphasis is placed on the interaction and opportunities for learning within the work situation than on the quality and output of work. Work therapists are in charge of these work groups, all of which have their daily or weekly staff–patient groups to discuss what is happening in terms of relationships within the work situation.

Apart from their specific function geared to administration, treatment, training, or work, these various groups all operate on the basis of two-way communication, with the expression of feeling and an opportunity to discuss freely what is happening in the interactional situation. The various meetings are linked so that, as far as possible, two-way communication is maintained from the level of the most regressed patients to the board of management.

Decision-Making Machinery at All Levels

While the ultimate decision-making machinery regarding major problems rests with the senior staff committee that meets daily, less important decisions are dealt with in the various group meetings. Administrative decisions and therapy tend to overlap.[5] Our aim is to provide a democratic decision-making policy in all areas of hospital functioning. The

5. D. H. Clark, in his *Administrative Therapy* (London, Tavistock Publications, 1964), has dealt with this matter at some length.

extent to which such opportunity can be utilized effectively for the ultimate good of the patients is dependent on many variables, including the complexity of the decisions involved —whether they effect staff, patients, or both—and to what extent they can be seen as an integral part of the therapeutic process. For instance, a decision on a patient's suitability to go on weekend pass, to be discharged, to be confronted in the event of deviant behavior, all call for a high degree of integration between patients and staff.

In a therapeutic community, the patients are given an opportunity to achieve the optimal role compatible with their mental state at the time. By daily participation in therapeutic groups, the patients become aware of new ways of dealing with their own and other people's problems. By sharing problems with the group, patients begin to become aware of themselves as other people see them. Through an examination in the daily therapeutic groups of their own and the problems of others, they learn something of the value of sharing their feelings with other people, thus achieving some degree of group identity. Instead of withdrawing and entertaining ideas of suicide and so on, a patient verbalizing his problem would probably find a ready response in other people, and a new attitude toward the problem may emerge. By sharing a problem requiring a decision with the group— including the staff—patients are afforded the opportunity to play a responsible role and achieve some degree of group identity.

What has been said about the patients applies equally to the staff. Their participation in therapeutic, administrative, and training groups helps them to assume new and more responsible roles. During the past four years the trained nurses, for example, have come to play an increasingly responsible and sophisticated role. They participate in all patient admission evaluation sessions, play an important role in writing up case records, frequently participate in domiciliary visits and other active roles in community psychiatry, and act as leaders in therapeutic groups. In a crisis situation on the ward, the nurse may well assume responsibility for handling the ensuing confrontation with a view to learning what lay behind the disturbed behavior.

The democratic, egalitarian structure of a therapeutic community implies delegation of authority from the central administration to the problem area itself. Personnel involved in the problem area, whether patients or staff, are given every encouragement to resolve their own difficulties and make decisions in the light of their findings. Such a social structure involves everyone in a more active role than they would have if decisions were left largely to central authorities. In this way the life of the hospital becomes a sort of living laboratory where crises, instead of being seen as troublesome and unnecessary, can be turned to good effect as learning situations. Such a distribution of decision-making opportunity may not be popular; it is resisted because most people find it much easier to blame authority figures for their plight than to be asked to undertake responsibility and decision-making on their own behalf.

Therapeutic Culture

A two-way communication system, with a view to discussion and learning, and an opportunity for decision-making at all levels of the hospital community form the basis of a social structure that involves virtually everyone in some active role. In a therapeutic community staff and patients are afforded an unusual opportunity for discussion of behavior in treatment, administrative, and work settings. An unusual amount of time is set aside for the examination of the social structure of the hospital. The role of the patient and each staff member is constantly under scrutiny, as are the role relationships between the various subgroups and disciplines. Examination of role relationships is possible in many of the group meetings already described. Thus, in a review following a ward or therapeutic group meeting, the role relationships among doctors, nurses, social workers, activity therapists, and so on, inevitably come up for scrutiny. Furthermore since all staff members are as far as possible involved in some form of sensitivity training, there is an increasing capacity to express feelings with a view to a greater degree of self-awareness.

The discussion of a person's performance in some form of personal interaction goes against many of our cultural norms. Such comment tends to be seen as "criticism," "rudeness," "hostility," and so on. It would seem to take approximately a year before the ordinary staff member, such as a new doctor[6] or student nurse, can become used to the idea of talking about role performance with a view to helping the individual concerned. The term "positive criticism" describes this process fairly accurately, but this should also convey the idea of learning inherent in the process.

As important as the examination of roles and role relation-

6. Maxwell Jones and Robert N. Rapoport, "The Absorption of New Doctors into a Therapeutic Community," in M. Greenblatt, D. L. Levinson, and R. H. Williams, eds., *The Patient and the Mental Hospital* (Glencoe, Ill., The Free Press, 1957).

ships is the examination of values and group attitudes. The day-in, day-out discussion of problems of living in a therapeutic community inevitably brings the focus to an examination of value judgments, prejudice, status consciousness, and so on. In many ways psychiatric hospitals tend to be less progressive than the country as a whole. At a time when the British government has abolished punishment for homosexuality between consenting adults and is considering reform of the abortion law, staff members of psychiatric hospitals do not seem to have mature opinions that might help in such deliberations; it is surprising how little time is spent trying to bring about an appropriate system of values shared by the majority of staff, so that a consistent attitude toward patients and their problems can be made manifest. There may be a strong case for the development of a therapeutic culture in which the attitudes and beliefs of the staff have a consistency and tolerance compatible with the sophisticated treatment program. This essential part of the social structure of a therapeutic community would, however, involve an immense expenditure of time and energy on the part of the entire hospital community.

Every hospital has its own culture and subcultures; priorities tend to be determined by the leaders in their particular spheres. In a therapeutic community a high priority is given by all to meetings where every aspect of the hospital life can be discussed. Sometimes the criticism is made that the staff members spend more time discussing their own roles, role relationships, and attitudes than they do in discussing the treatment of patients. This again raises the question of priorities and the values. In general, the more sensitive and dynamically oriented the staff, the greater is their capacity to interact with the patients for the patients' own betterment. What happened when a new role was introduced into the staff structure illustrates the flexibility inherent in the social structure of the therapeutic community.

Like most psychiatric hospitals, we were having serious difficulty in recruiting suitable young people for training as psychiatric nurses. We tried extensive advertising in the local and national press and in the nursing journals. We tried to get away from the rather stilted and unimaginative form of the usual nursing advertisements and attempted to appeal to the imagination of young people by stressing the interest of psychiatric work. To implement this we wrote articles in the nursing and medical journals which described our liberal approach to treatment and stressed the challenge represented by psychiatric nursing. We approached the schools for educational visits by the graduating classes, the Youth Employment Officer of the Ministry of Labour, the Nurse Recruitment Officer of the Regional Board, the local Member of Parliament, and so on. We printed an attractive brochure about nurse training and were, I think, the first hospital to be granted permission to do a one-year training in psychiatry for general trained nurses, compared with the usual eighteen months required for the registered mental nurse certificate. We accepted every invitation to talk to public groups and never let an opportunity pass which might lead to some nursing recruitment. We sent our nurse tutor to Ireland, because we understood that this was an area of low employment, and advertised in local papers in areas where unemployment was high. All these measures failed to produce the student nurses we wanted, and we slowly came to the conclusion that new approaches were called for.

We decided to initiate a new role, called activity assistant. The idea was that many young girls leaving school at sixteen went straight into industry and that by the time they were seventeen and a half, and eligible for student nurse training, they had already become established in a career. In Scotland cadet nursing schemes, which cater for this age group, were not permissible, and we set out to offer girls hospital work which did not involve formal nursing. We felt that exposing girls to all aspects of hospital work would give them some idea about their suitability for future training in some hospital occupation. There was a possibility that they might get interested in occupational therapy, catering, office work, social work, hairdressing, etc., but our main hope was that they would ultimately drift into nursing. We also saw the possibility of getting these young girls, motivated toward hospital work, to bring new ideas to this field. The senior staff committee agreed that the program should be supervised by the nurse tutor, a social worker, and the hospital secretary, under the general direction of the education committee. Our aim was to ensure that this group of young women developed a role which would not be unduly influenced by any of the existing traditions of nursing, social work, and so on. This was really tantamount to finding a new role for a group of young girls with similar educational and cultural backgrounds.

We started with eight girls. At the end of eight months this group had been reduced to six, all highly motivated toward hospital work, who had developed a positive place in the hospital organization. A great deal of discussion centered around these young activity assistants, and ambivalent feelings were expressed in all sectors of the hospital community. The cornerstone of their development was a daily meeting of forty-five minutes, when the activity assistants met with their supervisors and discussed their experiences during the day. Their training was based essentially on living-learning principles (see Chapter 4), and discussion focused on their emotional involvement and role problems. Where difficulties were expressed about a particular staff member, that member was asked to join the discussion meeting.

The girls' work with patients was limited to necessary activities, such as feeding and bathing, and social activities, such as walks, visits to the canteen, and various forms of movement to music. They were not assigned to admission wards but confined their activities to the long-stay and geriatric wards. In addition they worked in the ladies' hair-dressing department, the catering department, activity therapy, the administrative office, and the laundry. Their role relationship with the nursing personnel represented the greatest problem. These young girls did not come under the formal nursing hierarchy, and at first the ward staff were uncertain what exactly to do with them. It was quite explicit that they were not allowed to do any nursing procedures, such as giving medication or injections, but they could interact with the patients in nonmedical situations. They rapidly made themselves useful in feeding geriatric patients, helping with their dressing, bathing, and social activities. They began to suggest all kinds of activities, some of which were already in existence and some of which were new. In one ward old people took readily to painting, in another ward to knitting; the activity assistants read to the blind, and so on. Sometimes the nursing staff discouraged them from attempting new ventures, but when these were shown to be a success the nursing staff readily accommodated themselves. It was in music and movement and simple games, that the activity assistants filled a serious gap in the daily activity of the older and long-stay patients. The sense of rhythm and general vitality of these young people seemed to awaken latent potentialities within the patients.

In the past nurse training created a rather conformist end-product; the students tended to imitate their seniors passively. The introduction of a non-nursing group to the ward produced less formalized and more spontaneous social interaction. Inevitably there were difficulties in role relationships between the activity assistants and the nurses. At times the nurses criticized or laughed at them; at such times the activity assistants felt greatly embarrassed in their work. On the whole, however, the nursing staff were supportive, more particularly as their own work load was lightened by the presence of these young people. A great deal of mutual benefit accrued, each group learning from the other, and such learning situations were fostered in the daily group meetings.

Difficulties occasionally occurred between the activity assistants and some of the adolescent male and female patients. A few of the latter group initially resented these young girls on the staff, some of whom they had known at school. They were seen as potential rivals for the younger male patients. Inevitably, certain relationships between activity assistants and young male adolescents developed, and these took a course similar to what frequently happens in the early training of student nurses. The emotional involvements were brought up in the daily group seminar and discussed, at first with great difficulty and embarrassment, but later with a greater degree of awareness of the need to avoid special relationships with patients. One activity assistant, unable to accept the necessity for social distance between staff and patients, had to be asked to leave. The girls themselves began to have an awareness of such concepts as transference and countertransference, and the need for a professional role which avoided close involvement with patients. This knowledge was imparted without the use of technical jargon or formal teaching situations. It seemed that our recruitment problem could be solved by a program of this kind, which would allow us a long period of contact with the activity assistants before they applied for training as student or pupil nurses or for training in some other kind of hospital career.

Having largely overcome the resistances within the hospital and established a new role which brought much-needed vitality and enthusiasm to our activity program, we then encountered serious opposition from outside the hospital. It came from official bodies and was based on the possible exploitation of young people and their exposure to emotional conditions in a mental hospital at an age when they were not yet mature enough to cope with these stresses. The opposition was not firmly based on any first-hand knowledge of the young people or a detailed awareness of the program; it was determined by the cultural attitude toward young people in a hospital, epitomized by the minimum age of seventeen and one half for student nurse training. This represents a good example of the fact that the social structure within a hospital cannot afford to get out of line with the culture in the outside community. Such discrepancies can, however, with the appropriate timing and circumstances, be the prelude to progress and social evolution.

Given positive sanctions from above, such an innovation can do a great deal to improve the effectiveness of the social organization of the whole hospital. By developing new activities, attitudes, and role relationships, a new role forces everyone to examine their current position and function in the treatment program. It enhances one of the basic principles of a therapeutic community: that one should be constantly examining what one is doing, and why, and modifying procedures in the light of experience.

One great danger of a therapeutic culture developing within a hospital is that it may be too hospital-centered and tend to ignore the culture of the outside world. Any attempt to deviate too far from the norms of the society must inevitably lead to anxiety, misunderstanding, and rumor; it must damage the image and hence the usefulness of the hospital. But we can try to extend the concepts of the therapeutic community to the community outside, and bring about an over-all equilibration.

Change

Social structure is not a static organizational system; it has a dynamism of its own. This is particularly true in a therapeutic community, where such a large proportion of time is devoted to discussion of problems. Such a dynamic structure implies constant change. Action invites reaction, and people are traditionally resistant to change, which is usually equated with uncertainty and a threat to their own security. The more

an individual knows about the proposed change—the more
he has been consulted and listened to—the greater will be
his identification with the new situation and the greater will
be the opportunity for change. The therapeutic community,
with its system of checks and balances, decision-making by
consenus, multiple leadership, and so on, can tolerate and
utilize change more readily than can more rigid, hierarchical
organizations. Good leadership is essential, so that both the
attitude of the hospital and of the outside community can
be realistically perceived, and experimentation can be kept
within bounds.

The social structure of a therapeutic community contributes to a flexible organization and—because of the open
communication network, decision-making machinery, and so
on—it is possible to learn by experience and correct one's
mistakes with a minimum of delay. In this context it is seen
as perfectly legitimate to change a decision shortly after
having made it, provided this is done in a democratic way
and results from greater understanding achieved by the
group since the time of the original decision. One of the
great advantages of multiple leadership in a multidisciplinary
setting is that people with different personalities and training can interact in a setting that encourages discussion, social
learning, and changes of attitude. This, together with other
aspects of the therapeutic community social structure, represents as comprehensive a system of checks and balances as
one could hope to achieve. Changes of attitudes or decisions
under these circumstances are fundamentally different from
changes brought about by unilateral decisions; the latter are
subject to all the dangers of the abuse of power by a single
authority figure.

Evolution

Evolution might be defined as the progress from a worse to a better state of affairs, although this immediately raises the question of comparative value judgments and other thorny philosophical problems. Nevertheless, one is acutely aware of the dynamics of change in a therapeutic community; some process, however little understood, is in operation. That this process has direction is, I think, true at most times. The direction may change with remarkable rapidity in the light of new experience. Direction emerging in this way—as the end-product of a social system—seems to have a computer-like form, where after facts have been fed in, an over-all decision emerges. This oversimplified analogy brings out the point that direction seems to be largely immediate and systematic. Relatively little long-term planning is involved, and one is relatively little concerned with efficiency and economics. We are, then, in the fortunate position of being able to learn as we go along and apply new insights and knowledge with a minimum of delay.

One is tempted to see the interaction between the personnel in the therapeutic community and the dynamics of change as representing a process of evolution; we do use the term "evolve" not infrequently when we are unable to come to some decision by consenus on a difficult problem, decide that we cannot go further in the matter at present, and concur that we must allow various forces in the social environment to operate through time, until eventually a solution will evolve. The social structure including daily meetings at various levels and in some cases the taking of minutes (so that details of deliberations can be reviewed in a time perspective), enhances this evolutionary process. The implication is that a group of people motivated toward a common treatment goal and sharing a philosophy of treatment can, ultimately, through analysis of underlying conflicts, by compromise, and by learning, usually work through their differences and arrive at a common agreement.

We know relatively little about the causes of mental illness or the determinants of human behavior. To plan a program of positive mental hygiene in a community presents us with many more problems than we have solutions. I find it difficult to even guess at the social organization goals and practice of Dingleton Hospital five years hence. One can conceive of the time when long-term planning, based on much stronger actual information than is at present available, would be a profitable exercise. In the meantime I feel justified in using the concept of an evolutionary process that is leading us in the direction of an improved practice of psychiatry.

The idea of social organization must be broad enough to describe a dynamic process composed of many factors, including current psychiatric practice, the utilization of the social environment to improve treatment, the emphasis on two-way communication, the expression of feeling, and the concept of living–learning situations—and this constitutes an evolutionary process. Many people will see this more as an article of faith than anything that can be fully conceptualized, far less validated by research. There is no pretense that these comments represent anything but the beginnings of a possible theory. They cannot as yet be stated so that the formulations may be available for empirical testing and evaluation.

Chapter 2. Leadership

The role of the leader in a therapeutic community has many significant differences compared with that of the leader in most social groups. First the concept of a therapeutic community attempts to make optimal use of the potentials of all patients and staff. Moreover decision-making is as far as possible by consensus, and this indicates that what the formal leader presents to the outside world bears little relation to his actual function within the therapeutic community. A therapeutic community in a psychiatric hospital represents an attempt to achieve a social structure that both reinforces and complements the therapeutic techniques commonly employed in psychiatry. In my opinion both psychological and physical approaches to treatment are highly sensitive to the social environment in which the treatment is carried out.[1]

A psychiatric hospital has one major function, the treatment of various types of psychiatric illness. Such treatment may be based primarily on the hospital, or in the community

1. Maxwell Jones, "Group Work in Mental Hospitals," *British Journal of Psychiatry, 112* (1966), 1007.

in which the patient lives. Subsidiary functions bearing on the primary function include staff training and the education of the general public, including patients' relatives.

In a therapeutic community communications at all levels are made as efficient as possible, and decision-making by consensus is aimed at. Unilateral decision in any important matter affecting other people is avoided. This implies numerous meetings of staff, patients, or both, where decisions can be made. The use of meetings for decision-making, for the examination of roles and role relationships, for training, and above all for treatment can collectively involve people for the major part of their working day. Orthodox psychiatrists frequently criticize what they regard as the excessive use of staff time in meetings, which they often regard as detracting from time that would be more properly spent in some form of individual treatment.

It may be that the term "leader" in a therapeutic community should be replaced by the term "catalyst," or "charismatic leader."[2] Certainly one of his basic functions is to create situations which facilitate social learning. (The fact that the leader is usually associated with other leaders raises the question of multiple leadership, which will be discussed later.) Such a concept—convenient and often effective within a therapeutic community—must be modified to coincide with the expectations and demands of the outside society. Thus boards of management or other employing authorities expect to deal with one authority figure, who from their point of view represents the hospital, the nursing staff, the administration, and so on. Such a concept may not be acceptable to

2. Charisma is an early Christian term meaning "state of grace."

the leader in a therapeutic community, but clearly the hospital has to adjust to the rules and expectations of the central authority with whom the ultimate power and responsibility rests. In this context the leader constantly finds himself engaged in discussion with a central authority, either individually or in committee, where he is forced into making decisions of a unilateral nature. This goes against the principles practiced within the therapeutic community. As far as possible this contingency can be anticipated before committee meetings, so that the leader is adequately briefed and can represent the communal decision or, if caught unprepared, can at least share the situation with his colleagues retrospectively, so that his predicament is understood. Thus it is possible to retain the culture of the therapeutic community and the unique role of its leader, at the same time meeting the demands of society outside the therapeutic culture.

A therapeutic community, by attempting to make use of the optimal potential within patients and staff and by creating learning situations where this potential may be developed, represents both a goal—treatment and training —and a philosophy. This situation calls for leadership with sensitivity to the needs of others. In terms of both treatment and training, the capacity to develop potential becomes the most important aspect of leadership. There are many leaders of various professional and treatment groups within the hospital, and their contributions have to be brought into harmonious whole. The most important attribute of a leader in this context is his capacity to preserve the wholeness of an organization, while at the same time encouraging flexibility, self-examination, social learning, and change. Within such a frame of reference the leader may operate much as does the leader in a therapeutic group, taking no part in proceedings when the "work" is being done by the other participants, helping other people to look at themselves and their feelings when it is appropriate, and encouraging new leaders to emerge. The phrase "leading from behind" conveys something of this meaning.

Every society needs leaders, and a subgroup usually has one person who assumes final responsibility and authority and whose personality is seen as adequate to meet any crisis situation. Our basic assumption is that the leader, more than any other member of that society, knows what he is doing and why. In the case of a therapeutic community, this refers to the task in hand, the treatment of patients, with all the corollary factors, such as staff integration to achieve maximum effectiveness of the treatment team, in-service training, and, perhaps most important, an open communication network involving as far as possible all levels of patients and staff. A prerequisite of the leader is that he has sufficient sensitivity and social sense to be aware of the feelings and wishes of the patients and staff. In addition, a good formal training and the necessary experience helps in fulfilling the expectations of the staff. At the same time, sensitivity to current affairs both inside and outside the hospital and the ability to lead the staff through difficult, conflictual situations, preferably helping them to use their own skills, is implicit in successful leadership.

It seems to me that it is not necessary for the leader to have explicit long-term treatment and philosophical goals. More important is the establishment of immediate group goals which develop from interaction within the staff and, to some extent, the patients too. The acceptance or rejection of a new idea coming from any member of the community will depend on many factors; the most important factor is that in a democratic setting the majority of people are free to become interested in testing out new possibilities. In a developing community staff can get used to the idea of change, provided change is seen to be beneficial to patient care and treatment and the well-being of the staff. Resistance to change is an inherent quality in us all. It can be modified most effectively by the repeated demonstration that change brings about an over-all improvement.

Change has a different significance for different individuals; it may be resisted most by the people who are called upon to make the maximum contribution and, by implication, the maximum change. If such individuals can see potential benefit to themselves and the community as a whole, then there is some possibility that the plan may be tried out. The ideas of staff in more senior positions tend to have a more ready acceptance than those coming from persons lower in the hierarchy. This tendency should diminish in time, and these planning situations test the effectiveness of the democratic, egalitarian structure; the outcome depends on several factors, the most important of which is the skill and personality of the leader or leaders.

Bales[3] has shown that leaders who talk more than they listen are less popular than leaders who talk less and listen more. By enhancing the participation of others, the leader helps them to become more confident and skilled. At the

3. R. F. Bales, "Staff Status and Likability as a Function of Talking and Listening in Decision-Making Groups," in L. D. White, ed., *The State of the Social Sciences* (Chicago, University of Chicago Press, 1956), pp. 148–61.

same time he ensures that the ideas and feelings of other group members are expressed. In a therapeutic community the leader may be called upon to play several roles. Thus, when there is a considerable degree of equilibrium and many competent colleagues whose skills can complement his own, the more the leader allows other leaders to emerge and develop their own skills, the better. But at times of crisis the leader may have to act more independently and assert his latent authority. The effect on the group of such a change of role will depend on the outcome of the crisis. If the crisis is successfully resolved and, more particularly, if the group members learn from the experience and feel more competent to deal with the next crisis, then the belief in and acceptance of the leader is enhanced. The active and inactive aspects of the leadership role are complementary; the leader, sensitive to the group situation, becomes active at appropriate times and inactive at others. This principle would seem to apply to some extent in all group and community meetings.[4]

In general the amount of staff participation varies inversely with the patients' competence. Thus, at a time of constructive functioning, which usually implies a group of patients who have already benefited from considerable treatment, the staff may be relatively inactive. At another time, for instance following the influx of disturbed new patients, the staff may have to play a more active role. This concept of active and inactive involvement of the leader or leaders

4. A group meeting implies a selected group of patients and staff who meet regularly for a specific therapeutic function. A community meeting implies a meeting to discuss current interpersonal problems affecting patients and staff operating in a certain geographical area, and is usually much larger than a group meeting.

applies to group and community meetings, as well as to staff meetings and the more informal life of the hospital. Thus at times of stress the leader is forced into a more active role. By asserting his latent authority he may well meet with a good deal of opposition and unpopularity. It is at such times that his role relationship with the deputy leader becomes of paramount importance.

The Deputy Leader

In general one of the major problems in a therapeutic community is the role relationship between the medical director and his deputy. The same problem exists in the traditional hierarchical hospital structure, but there the social organization itself tends to make the relationship explicit: the authority of the leader is unquestioned. Ideally, in any hospital, the role relationship between the medical director and his deputy need not result in conflict, which only occurs when the leader and his deputy compete for the same functions. In our case the deputy functions primarily in areas other than that of the medical director—as a middle man—in much the same way as the various department heads, who, while leaders in their own departments, do not compete with the medical director for the same function. When the medical director's formal status requires him to represent the hospital to the outside world, he may find himself speaking for one or another department head. When adequately briefed, he should do this with reasonable success. His knowledge of any one department should be the result of a good communication system and, to some extent, personal involvement in the department, but this does not mean that he in any way threatens the department head's leadership in his own functional area.

If the deputy has a greater capacity for leadership than the medical director, and this is well known to everyone, the distinction between the designated leader and the real leader would become increasingly obvious. Such a situation could only function satisfactorily if, either implicitly or explicitly the designated leader accepted the situation with good grace. It is conceivable, although I have never seen such a circumstance, that the designated leader would allow himself to be guided by the real leader.

In a therapeutic community there is a high degree of delegation of responsibility and authority, not only to the deputy but to all levels of staff and the patient population as well. It is a characteristic of any small society not only for a leader who represents the choice of the majority to emerge, but for the minority group to have its own leader in opposition to the formal leader. This principle is found in all democratic governing bodies and ensures that divergent views get a hearing and decisions are reached, hopefully, after a thorough examination of the different points of view. The possibility of the deputy displacing the leader is always in the background, whether explicit or implicit, practical or impractical. The deputy is well aware of this and, inevitably, must at times covet many of the advantages, in terms of power and pay, that are associated with the leader. Freed from final responsibility for the hospital and yet vested with considerable power, the deputy may, however, find himself in a relatively enviable position. He can afford to be much more experimental and controversial in his outlook. He stands to gain when the formal leader is used as a scapegoat during times of stress. It is, of course, possible that the deputy may himself become a scapegoat.

Bales[5] describes the instrumental, or task, leader and the popular leader, and his work throws much light on this subject. Using experimental groups, the investigators gave each group a definite task to accomplish: to reach by discussion a solution to a sex problem. The individual who showed most initiative tended to be the leader. He had of necessity to evaluate and criticize the contributions of others. Thus the instrumental, or task, leader, while moving the group toward its goal, generates tensions within the group that generally are reduced by the popular leader, who is identified more with the group feeling and who acts as conciliator. In a later paper Bales[6] sought to establish a relation between the initiator of interaction and the recipient of interaction. The former talked more than he listened, and while he might be successful in reaching the group goal he did so by frustrating and controlling the members. The latter was apt to encourage true expression and so be more rewarding to the group members.

No matter how democratically a decision has been arrived at in a therapeutic community, there is always a tendency for some degree of cultural lag. The leader will be seen as blameworthy where the new order appears to be less successful than the old. The temptation to play a popular role and capitalize on the leader's temporary unpopularity at times of stress

5. R. F. Bales, "The Equilibrium Problem in Small Groups," in Talcott Parsons, R. F. Bales, and E. A. Shils, *Working Papers in the Theory of Action* (Glencoe, Ill., The Free Press, 1953), pp. 111–61.

6. Bales, "Staff Status and Likability."

imposes a tremendous responsibility on the deputy. His role calls for at least as much skill and integrity as that of the leader. The deputy should be able to use the disaffection in the group to create a learning situation rather than exploit it for his own ends. If the leader and the deputy can complement each other, then even in situations of disagreement they can remain relatively objective. Conflict occurs only when the leader and his deputy compete for the same functions. This is somewhat analagous to the family situation where it is desirable that parents complement each other by serving quite different functions. Such complementarity means that at times of crisis the parents are much more competent to analyze the factors contributing to the crisis and so help the children to grow to understanding and a new awareness of how problems can be overcome.

The role relationship between the leader and deputy calls for a great deal of insight from both. In a therapeutic community setting the satisfactions as well as the responsibilities are more equally divided than in the traditional hospital model. The leader must ensure that his junior colleague has as much investment in the program as he has himself. Public acclaim, visits to other hospitals, formal lectures and so on should, as far as possible, be shared. Moreover, the temptation on the part of the leader to devalue his deputy calls for every bit as much integrity and insight as does the reverse. The most serious crises from the point of view of hospital equilibrium will emerge when the leader and his deputy are in conflict. Unless it can be satisfactorily handled, this situation must inevitably lead to a split within the hospital population. In my experience by far the best way of avoiding such difficulties is by feeding back the conflict into the staff group—assuming that it has the capacity to deal with problems of this kind and that it meets at frequent, preferably daily, intervals. Every group has its limits; but a problem of this kind, if it cannot be worked through by the senior staff, is unlikely to be resolved by a face-to-face confrontation by the two antagonists alone. Three or more competent group workers in responsible roles are needed, so that one of the leaders is in a position to take over the group when two of the authority figures are in conflict. Any therapeutic community is as good as the people in it, and learning can go on only when there are the resources, skill, and motivation to resolve crisis situations. If the role relationship between the leader and his deputy leads to a permanent cleavage, then one can hardly talk about a therapeutic community. It may be that certain situations can only be resolved by the departure of one of the two antagonists. Such a situation does not necessarily imply failure on the part of either people concerned—any more than does a divorce, which can often be a prelude to a much more satisfactory situation for both parties. We know that many capable and well-trained doctors can do excellent treatment. But the circumstances in which their potential is fully realized varies considerably, and it is probable that only a minority of psychatrists as currently trained can reach their optimal performance in a therapeutic community setting.

Multiple Leadership

To be effective, a therapeutic community needs several leaders, all of whom are well trained in group work and have the training, personality, and skills to be accepted as leaders when the formal leader is either absent or himself involved in an emotional interaction or conflict with another group member. When the formal leader is himself emotionally involved in conflict with another colleague, he cannot retain the objectivity and skill required to handle the situation. At this point an uninvolved colleague is needed to assume temporary leadership within the group. This potential for changing leadership calls for at least three, and preferably more, people capable of assuming this leadership role. A temporary change of leadership in response to a crisis of this kind is only possible if the formal leader or leaders are prepared to assume the role of the subject and have their performance scrutinized by their peers.[7] Acceptance of this mode of action is essential if multiple leadership is to become a reality. It is not enough for the formal leader to step aside under such circumstances: he must be prepared to have his performance examined by experienced and uninvolved colleagues who have the competence to analyze the factors that have produced the conflict, so that both antagonists are in a position to learn from the confrontation.

It is implicit in a therapeutic community that the group is more important than any one leader and will change its leadership according to prevailing circumstances. This implies a two-way process: individual is sensitive to the group, and vice versa. (How far such sensitivity can be developed through training, and how far it is rooted in the personality, will be discussed later under Sensitivity Training.) The other important factor is the social organization of the therapeutic community with its democratic–egalitarian structure. In our present society the highly trained professional who attains

7. This topic is developed below, in Chapter 4, pp. 69–78.

a leadership position automatically acquires authority, responsibility, power, and prestige. To share such privileges and status goes against the formal training and culture of the medical world. This is alien to past experience and difficult for most people to accept. But far more difficult is the prospect of becoming the subject and having ones' performance scrutinized when the group feels this appropriate. Leadership in a therapeutic community calls for an unusual degree of identification with the community. Such a concept raises problems about which, at the present state of our knowledge, we can only speculate.

The formal leader's peers, by assuming the maximum role compatible with their ability, competence, and acceptance by the rest of the group, are in a position to develop their own skills and become increasingly involved in the aims and functioning of the therapeutic community. This does not necessarily rule out the possibility of the charisma of the formal leader, but it certainly limits such development. But the best possible antidote to charismatic effect is to have the attitudes, beliefs, and role of the formal leader under constant discussion and examination—as is the case with the other staff personnel. One can assume that a certain amount of charisma is attached to all leaders, and that the dominance over the other opinions represents the greatest danger of distortion.

Balanced leadership by several people, all of whom are capable of playing a leadership role when required, offers exceptional possibilities for growth within the community. This safeguards against the superimposition of emotionally toned ideas and beliefs emanating from any one source. Although I lack proof, it is my belief that a therapeutic community affords a system of checks and balances that enhances the possibility of group, as opposed to individual, leadership. Here the concept of multiple leadership by several competent individuals, who are accepted by the group and can assume leadership according to the changing dynamics of the group situation, fuses with the concept of group leadership.

A group is made up of a number of individuals, all with their own particular personalities. The extent to which the leaders become the vehicle of expression of the group and are, in a sense, subservient to the group, determines the degree of group leadership. Ideas such as this are bound to arouse considerable anxiety as far as the individual and his identity are concerned. Such anxiety is implicit in terms like "persuasion," "indoctrination," "brainwashing," and so on. As a corollary to this, the personality of the formal leader of a therapeutic community is quite appropriately suspect, and the individual's innate fear of being changed is aroused. A therapeutic community implies the adoption by the individual of attitudes and beliefs that emanate from the interaction among the members of that community. Many people perceive this not in terms of group pressure and a therapeutic culture, but in terms of the personality of the formal leader. They argue, quite understandably, that a therapeutic community tends to develop as a result of the efforts of one initiator, and in this sense can be seen as a projection of his own persona. (Persona is the way in which an individual chooses to present himself to a group.) I find it hard to accept this view, but it is obvious that I am not the best judge. I hope that this book will go at least some way to explain why I would dissociate the concept as expressed here from an individual cult. I feel myself to be changing all the time in response to the pressures of the group and the numerous daily opportunities for the process of social learning.

From my own experience I feel that ideas initiated by one individual and adopted by a group can evolve so that the influence of the individual becomes fused with that of the other leaders; a group, rather than an individual-inspired, culture emerges. It is apparent that multiple leadership is an extremely complicated and obscure subject, about which we have to know a great deal more if plans in Great Britain for the coordination of health services and local authority services are to be implemented satisfactorily. For example, in this age of specialization a field like social work becomes broken up into numerous subdisciplines, each jealously guarding its own sovereignty. Add to this the fact that some social workers are employed by hospitals and others by local authorities, and one finds a situation in which seniority, status, and prestige become immensely important. If one widens the area to include the whole field of mental health, then numerous other disciplines become involved: psychiatry, psychology, nursing, occupational therapy, and so on. No amount of individual skill in one's own particular profession can circumvent the need for group skills with a view to understanding the dynamics of individuals when they interact, the problems of decision-making, social learning, leadership, and other topics touched upon in this book. Multiple leadership in a multidisciplinary setting is an essential goal which coordinated services must set for themselves—if they are going to be optimally useful. This implies not only suitable training in one's own profession and a far greater degree of interdisciplinary training than at present exists, but continued on-the-job training by the utilization of living-learning situations. Multiple leadership is at present a most crucial area, and it is here that knowledge and competent training are most lacking.

During the past twenty years I have become more and more concerned with the idea of a group identity that transcends individual identity. When I was Director of the Social Rehabilitation Unit at the Belmont Hospital in Scotland from 1947 to 1959 I learned by bitter experience the difficulty of being both the leader in the clinical setting of the therapeutic community and the formal leader who was responsible to the employing authority and to the public at large. I was in the almost untenable position of having to look in two ways at the same time: to defend the unit from its detractors outside and, at the same time, to remind the unit staff and patients of the reality of the outside world. The necessity to portray the attitudes and feelings of outside society to the therapeutic community tends to alienate the leader from his own colleagues and patients. In my case it was possible slowly to win over our employers, in particular the Board of Management and the Regional Board.

There were two major crises during my term of office. The first was a committee of enquiry set up by the Board of Management, with the unmistakable aim of terminating the therapeutic community. I faced this committee alone and found it one of the most traumatic experiences of my life, mainly because I was seen as the dangerous and deviant leader who was threatening the effectiveness and security of the parent hospital.[8] The second committee of enquiry was

8. The Social Rehabilitation Unit, although largely autonomous, was administratively part of Belmont Hospital. In 1959 full autonomy was granted and the Unit was renamed Henderson Hospital.

called about a year later by the Regional Hospital Board. On this occasion other key staff members were also interrogated. The various unit leaders were able to convey the concept of the therapeutic community to the committee of enquiry in a way that had been impossible when I was interrogated alone.

The social rehabilitation unit at Belmont Hospital, now renamed Henderson Hospital, had the advantage of a generous research grant from the Nuffield Foundation, which allowed us to employ as many as seven behavioral scientists at one time. Their findings have been summarized by Rapoport.[9] For me, to discover the discrepancy between what I thought I was doing as a leader and what trained observers saw me doing was frequently a painful—but almost invariably a rich and learning—experience. During the period of this research (1953–57) we had achieved a degree of multiple leadership that was rare if not unique in a psychiatric hospital at that time. The four psychiatrists, the director of nursing, the psychiatric social worker, and the psychologist, along with other more junior members of the staff, all had independent and interdependent leadership roles. Thus in a crisis, any one of seven or eight competent group therapists could assume a leadership role, and there was a considerable amount of role blurring, particularly in the area of group therapy, where the medical staff was seen as no more competent than others as group leaders. The fact that we were responsible for eighty or ninety severe character disorders of both sexes in an open unit, in close proximity to the parent hospital, created formidable difficulties.

I was constantly dealing with problems relating to the parent hospital, which made no secret of its dislike for us but

9. Rapoport, *Community As Doctor.*

gave us the doubtful advantages of being a minority group
with the cohesiveness and group identity that often stem
from such a vulnerable position. This dual role of being the
buffer to the hostile outside environment and at the same
time the leader of the therapeutic community convinced me
of the need for positive sanctions from above. Luckily, some
very powerful figures in medical, administrative, and parlia-
mentary positions gave us very positive support, without
which the social rehabilitation unit at Belmont Hospital
would have undoubtedly disappeared. Under these difficult
circumstances, we carried the concept of multiple leadership
as far as we could. The battle for existence, which continued
throughout my entire twelve years at Henderson Hospital,
called for leadership that was task oriented. Under this kind
of stress, I found that there must be one leader whose leadership was accepted by the group as a whole to take on the
challenge for survival.

During my past five years as Physician Superintendent at
Dingleton Hospital, circumstances have been entirely different and have favored the development of multiple leadership. To begin with I was in the formal leadership role
involving the entire hospital and had also very positive
sanctions from both the Board of Management and the
Regional Hospital Board. In addition, my role relationships
with the principal Nursing Officer and the hospital secretary
have been unusually good, so that the Holy Trinity, has
come to be seen as a coordinated body. During these years
there has been a steady transition from a fairly orthodox,
hierarchical organization to a much more egalitarian social
structure, with the emergence of a definitive therapeutic
culture. The time now seemed appropriate to decentralize

the hospital. As we have three senior doctors and three junior doctors and are responsible for the mental welfare of three counties and a part of a fourth, it seemed appropriate that we should develop three county teams, each containing a senior and junior doctor, a psychiatric social worker, and a senior nurse. This development meant that in addition to being the physician superintendent, I was now a team leader and had to play an additional role. The three teams act quite independently, but a certain amount of feedback occurs; in addition to the team identity there is a certain degree of hospital identity.

It is in the thirty-bed admission ward for both sexes that the real test of multiple leadership occurs. All three teams admit patients to this unit, and the nurses have to relate to all six doctors, the three psychiatric social workers, and the three senior nurses. While it is not unusual for admission wards to have as many consultants, in my experience there is seldom any serious effort to develop a therapeutic community under these circumstances. Fortunately, we have very experienced male and female charge nurses, who are seen as the leaders in the ward setting. They are present at the daily ward meetings with the thirty patients; each doctor attends this meeting once or twice a week, in addition to having a small group meeting with the patients from his county twice a week. This means that the group leadership role and the ultimate responsibility for the group rests more with the nursing staff than with the medical staff. Nevertheless, at times of stress, the latent authority of the doctor is evoked, and the nurses have no hesitation in using the doctor's particular prestige and skill. It was realized from the start that such a complicated role relationship among numerous leaders from different disciplines would require a great deal of time for discussion, evaluation, and learning. It is important to stress here that all the staff involved in the admission ward meet together weekly for an hour and a half to discuss roles, role relationships, and the over-all culture of the ward. In addition to confrontations that may occur at such meetings, there is no hesitation in calling for an immediate confrontation involving the relevant personnel at times of exceptional stress. Here multiple leadership in a multidisciplinary setting is close to becoming a reality.

Patient Leadership

A mental hospital such as Dingleton has a patient population largely made up of long-stay patients, with almost fifty per cent over the age of sixty-five. Moreover, the relatively rapid turnover in the admission ward tends to create two almost separate communities centered on the admission ward and on the rest of the hospital. The admission ward patients stay for a comparatively short time so that they are not so deeply involved with the hospital as the long-stay patients. In a modern psychiatric hospital long-stay patients are rehabilitated to the outside community whenever possible, and relatively few of the patients left in hospital are capable of assuming responsible and complicated roles. Nevertheless, there is every reason to think that patient leadership forms an important part of any well-organized hospital society. The temptation to overlook this fact must be guarded against constantly, particularly by the senior staff.

The evils of the custodial era are now seen as the result of removing the patient's individuality by a hospital policy where everything is done for him and he is not allowed to think and act as an independent person. The concept of a therapeutic community carries the idea of the patient's self-determination to a new stage and invests the patient body with increasing responsibility for its own treatment and living conditions, in collaboration with the staff. In this way, some patients become active participants in the planning and carrying out of their own treatment. They are, moreover, in a position to make the staff aware of its own shortcomings, which may be based on a blind adherence to tradition, ignorance of the patient world, and the abuse of the professional role. These shortcomings, often unconsciously determined, have brought advantages to the staff rather than to the patients.[10]

How far the patient can usefully participate in the treatment of other patients will depend on many factors, the most

10. This theme is being developed in many other social areas such as the U.S. government's Economic Opportunity Act. Nathan Glazer, in *New Society* (December 31, 1966), describes how the Mobilization for Youth program is using its money to train and organize the poor to fight against established bureaucracy. Change must come from the initiative of the poor themselves rather than by an attempt to reform the tradition-ridden bureaucratic machine. Here we have a new phenomenon: state money being used to train and organize the poor to better themselves, even though this may initially appear to be at the expense of the public and private agencies such as the schools, police, housing authorities, and so on. He states: "but in the slums of American great cities, it will be a rare social worker who can both organize the slum dwellers to the point where they effectively demand social betterment, and know where to draw the line—or be able to draw it—when they want to go further. What is to me most striking is how widely it is accepted among those who have been closest to the situations that combative organization is essential to improvement."

important being the degree of ego disorganization of the patient population. Rapoport[11] has made a relatively objective study of the effect of some aspects of patient responsibility on the over-all culture of a therapeutic community. The patients he studied had character disorders and were very different from the long-stay population of our hospital. Analytic group psychotherapy operates on the principle that with skilled guidance patients can come to have a powerful therapeutic influence on other patients. There is no question but that the patients in such a group learn their skills to a considerable extent from the trained staff leader. However, as with any successful psychotherapy, the patient can later apply these skills to his ordinary life outside the therapeutic situation. The growth of social and psychoanalytic skills which undoubtedly occurs with many patients in the group treatment, inevitably manifests itself in the ordinary daily life of the patient, whether in the hospital or in the environment outside. When group psychotherapy is practiced on an in-patient basis, staff members have an opportunity to observe the patients' behavior outside the group, and in formal group situations tend to become increasingly "therapeutic." I do not as yet feel competent to go into any discussion of the hospital-staff culture compared with the patient culture. There is, however, a tendency for the two cultures to come closer as an inevitable result of day-in, day-out discussion of ward problems.

As a byproduct of the greater expectation of patient performance, patient leaders tend to emerge, and in the therapeutic community they tend to be influenced by the same

11. Rapoport, *Community As Doctor.*

learning process that affects the staff. In other words there
is a strong tendency for training and treatment to overlap.
As Rapoport[12] has shown, there is a tendency for alternating
periods of organization and disorganization. During the
former, leaders emerge who are accepted by the majority of
patients; a process of disintegration in terms of leadership
occurs in the latter situation. One of the problems in the
development of patient leadership is the effect that it has on
the staff. Nurses in particular like to feel that they are helping the patients on their wards and may feel threatened by
the emergence of patient leaders, who to some extent take
over functions normally served by the nurses themselves. In
other words, the emergence of patient leaders is linked with
the culture of the ward and the role expectations of the
staff. How far patient and staff roles can be allowed to overlap is an open question. It would seem, however, that the
danger in any hospital community arises if the patient is not
allowed to develop his optimal potential as an individual
or a leader; and this dimension of the role of the patient in
hospital has generally been neglected.

What has so far been said about patient leadership relates
particularly to new patients in the admission wards, or short-
stay patients in a day hospital setting: in other words, to
patients who have a close link with the society from which
they have come and have not become absorbed into a hospital community.

The long-stay patient, on the other hand, is usually a
schizophrenic with severe ego disintegration or a geriatric
patient with some form of organic brain damage. With

12. Robert N. Rapoport, "Oscillations in Sociotherapy," *Human
Relations*, 9 (1956), 357.

long-stay patients, the staff expectation of patient leadership
is understandably much more modest. Considerations other
than the patient's clinical condition must necessarily be taken
into account. The admission wards, with their rapid turnover,
variety of clinical material, and relatively greater response
to treatment, traditionally have the greatest appeal for the
training of doctors, nurses, and social workers. The staffing
tends to be more generous than in the long-stay wards, and
the quality of the nurses tends to be higher. Hence it seems
that not only do the short-stay patients have much greater
potential for active participation in the life of the hospital
and the development of leadership roles, but there is also a
much greater expectation of patient leadership among the
nurses.

It is difficult to reconcile the helplessness and dependence
of many long-stay patients with the idea of patient leadership.
At the same time what little potential there is tends to be
lost when the nurses adopt a largely custodial or protective
role. Anyone who has attempted some form of community
treatment in a long-stay ward with a predominantly geriatric
or schizophrenic population knows how difficult it is to
recognize and foster whatever leadership potential there
may be. The fact that the nurses in such wards tend to be
relatively untrained and content to view their role in a very
simple frame of reference and adopt a largely protective
role toward their charges only increases the difficulty. Social
interaction tends to be completely different from what one
commonly finds in an admission ward. A daily ward meeting
in a long-stay ward may turn out to be largely unproductive
because of the patients' lack of spontaneity and disordered
perception of the world. It is usually much more productive

to have small, relatively intimate groups, with some simple task supervised by a staff member. Under a simple regime of this kind, regressed patients can often begin to develop greater contact with reality and become more aware of themselves as individuals.

Unfortunately mental hospitals do not readily achieve continuity in their nursing staff. Nursing personnel frequently changes, and the patient loses the self-awareness that one nurse can give him by daily contact with the same individual.

The pioneering work being carried out by Laing and his associates at Kingsley Hall (London) more nearly approaches the type of ego reintegration we are talking about. He has a certain number of trained personnel, "ordinary" people, and schizophrenics living together as one community. Here the distinction between staff and patients is deliberately blurred. Schizophrenics are allowed to behave as they wish and may regress to infantile behavior. The reintegration of the personality which Laing claims to bring about may well have the same impact on ideas of patient management as did those of Harry Stack Sullivan[13] more than three decades ago.

13. Harry S. Sullivan, "Sociopsychiatric Research: Its Implications for the Schizophrenia Problem and for Mental Hygiene," *American Journal of Psychiatry, 10* (1931), 977. Ronald Laing's approach was brilliantly dramatized in "In Two Minds," a play by David Mercer on BBC Television on February 23, 1967. See also Laing and A. Esterson, "Sanity, Madness and the Family," in *Families of Schizophrenics, 1* (London, Tavistock Publications, 1964). D. Cooper, *Psychiatry and Anti-Psychiatry* (London, Tavistock Publications, 1967).

Chapter 3. Decision-Making by Consensus

Leadership is intimately linked with decision-making, and it is this latter area that shows perhaps the most striking contrasts between traditional hospital and therapeutic community practice. In a therapeutic community, a unilateral decision, no matter how wise, is seen as contradictory to the basic philosophy. Thus the matron (or director of nursing), who might ordinarily be expected to make the final decision regarding all matters having to do with the nursing staff, will tend to adopt a new decision-making policy in a therapeutic community. The proposal that nurses wear street clothes on duty, instead of a uniform, for example, is a matter affecting all staff and patients; and in a therapeutic community it would be thoroughly discussed, and a decision would be arrived at by group consensus. Clearly a total hospital population is too large to operate as one group. But opinions can be canvassed and fed back to the group of senior staff representing all relevant disciplines, and they can then attempt to come to some final decision by consensus. In our example, the matron (or director of nursing) would be the central figure, and her views would be given special consideration.

However if the senior staff as a whole were against the proposed change, then we would conclude that the hospital was not yet ready for the new move and that decision should be postponed. Such a matter might or might not appear again for reevaluation at some later date. This would depend on many factors, the main ones being the need for such a change and who expressed it, the staff or the director of nursing herself: if the staff, then history might well repeat itself and no change would occur until such time as the hospital as a whole began to view the proposed change in a favorable light. In a climate of this kind, a unilateral decision by an authority figure would be immediately opposed by the staff group; any action would be postponed until such time as group consensus could be arrived at.

The concept of consensus in decision-making is a difficult one. What a person says or communicates nonverbally in a group may differ remarkably from what the same individual would choose to express by secret ballot. Moreover the charismatic effect of the leader is particularly liable to be felt when an issue is raised with which he is strongly identified. It may be expedient for some group members to support a person rather than a cause or principle. People may be afraid of invoking the disapproval of the leader and even jeopardizing their job security by opposing him. In addition people may find that the attitude which they subscribe to in a meeting is modified in retrospect, particularly after discussion with their own particular subgroup. Finally, what one says in a group and what one will actually do in practice may show great discrepancies.

It becomes clear then that when one talks about decision by consensus, one is talking about a highly complex social situation; what appears to be a group decision may be finite and temporary. The leader is in a strong position to manipulate the meeting by posing a question that calls for an answer which oversimplifies the issue. This applies equally to administrative and to clinical decisions. Such an abuse of power— or manipulative skill—whether conscious or unconscious, will in all probability not pass without a confrontation with the peer group. If one of the leaders attempts to manipulate the group in order to get a group decision, he is liable to have his performance scrutinized and his motives analyzed.

In the case of decision-making affecting the senior staff as a group, there would be many occasions when movement occurs without a specific decision or value judgment being made. The matter may be postponed until the facts are better understood, as for instance with the formation of an ad hoc committee to enquire into a subject and then to report back to the senior staff committee. Even then the actual decision may be made without much discussion if the matter arouses little interest or is of no great consequence. However when action is proposed, the subject may achieve a new significance and may be re-examined in the light of the feelings aroused. This introduces the element of time. It may be that difficult decisions can be made when there is a gradual development of a theme, and action may be taken after an appropriate preliminary period of time has elapsed. This allows for a mutual adjustment of values and a willingness to compromise on the part of everyone, in order to find the best possible solution as seen by all the people involved. In the early stages of a therapeutic community with forceful leadership there may be a much greater tendency for an expressive or popular leader to represent the feelings of the group who may feel to some extent the need to slow down the action of the task leader. When the concept of multiple leadership, something much closer to group action, has taken effect then decision-making by consensus is more likely to be achieved and successful.

The difficulty is that there is no way of evaluating the feeling content of the group at any one time, and one has little choice but to use the overt expression of the individual group members as well as try to evaluate the climate of the group as a whole. Such an esoteric concept as "group climate" is open to abuse, but one has to assume that the leaders are sufficiently sensitive to the feelings and attitudes of the group to assess with some degree of accuracy the over-all group climate. Thus, a leader may say: "It seems to me that the general feeling of the group is that we should have a pilot run in the female admission ward and let the nurses wear street clothes for a month. After that time we can discuss the issue again in light of experience. What do people feel?" If the response from the group, in terms of expressed opinion, feeling, and behavior is positive, then this seems to me to be about as near to group consensus as one can get.

This idea of group climate is closely linked with small group therapy. In such a setting one attempts to interpret the long silence, or, alternatively, excessive and apparently point-less conversation. Sensitivity to the dynamics of the group, which can to some extent be tested by the group's response to an interpretation, is an essential part of the awareness of group climate.

It would appear that decision-making by consensus is at best a vague concept that endeavors to reflect the over-all wish of the group at any one time. It becomes more effective

the greater the security of the group, the freer the communication, the greater the skills of the individuals involved, and
the more sensitive and far-seeing the over-all leadership. In
a therapeutic community there is a system of checks and
balances that allows for a decision made when under pressure
of stress to be modified at a later date, when the group may
be more competent to deal with the issue objectively. Perhaps
the greatest advantage of a democratic decision-making
policy is that it affords a rich opportunity for mutual education. This subject will be taken up later in the discussion
of living–learning situations.

Hidden Agendas

One of the difficulties in discussing administrative and clinical problems in a therapeutic community is that one faces
frequently a situation where the problem under discussion
uncovers some underlying conflict. In a formal hospital no
one would dream of departing from the formal agenda in
order to try to come to some understanding of the underlying
conflict. The chairman would in all probability rule such a
change of procedure out of order. The job would be done;
the administrators would complete the agenda to the best of
their ability; and by the end of the meeting the more per-
ceptive members might have an uncomfortable feeling of
unfulfillment. At most, they would discuss their feelings
with their own particular confidants; if anxiety reached a
certain pitch, then formal contact might be made with the
chairman, or a request for an enquiry might appear on the
next agenda. However, such an enquiry would probably be
in terms of some practical proposition, such as a fact-finding

committee. Even if a conflict between two of the members was recognized it would tend to be dealt with outside the administrative meeting; it would be seen more in terms of nuisance value than worthy of high priority in terms of the ultimate effectiveness of the administration. As an example, the official view would be that it would serve little purpose to intervene in some hotly disputed issue on the board of management and suggest that the problem really lay in the rivalry between the chairman and one of the members.

In a therapeutic community such a conflict is seen in quite another perspective. It has been pointed out that decision-making often involves discussion, change of attitude, and a learning situation, before consensus can be arrived at. This is particularly true with matters affecting patients and staff. (Many administrative problems concern purely material and economic factors and no question of a hidden agenda may arise.) When interpersonal difficulties do arise, it is consistent with the philosophy of a therapeutic community that this hidden agenda should be examined, even if it means postponing action on the formal agenda. Put in psychoanalytic terms, the more the staff in a therapeutic community becomes familiar with concepts of manifest and latent content, the more they are liable to pay heed to the latent content. The decision to interrupt a discussion of an item on a formal agenda in order to examine the hidden agenda is a very difficult one; it must be viewed in the light of our view of decision-making. The circumstances may be such that an administrative decision cannot wait. But this would not prevent the possibility of creating a separate living–learning situation by a confrontation of the individuals concerned. (This is taken up in greater detail in the next chapter.)

Feedback

Feedback is one of the basic concepts in a therapeutic community. To some extent it violates one of our deeply ingrained
cultural characteristics, epitomized by the expression, "tell-
ing tales out of school." It is allied to the idea of "currying
favor," which implies that the child tells the teacher about
the behavior of a peer with a view to gaining approval from
the teacher. It reaches its most threatening dimensions in
prison, where to "snitch" may well endanger the life of the
"snitcher" at the hands of his peers. To inform has a negative
connotation that is hard to overcome. Group therapy makes
the basic assumptions that discussion of personal problems
leads ultimately to benefit for the individual. The topics
discussed are treated as confidential by the group members.
As every group therapist knows, it takes a long time before
a group assumes such a cultural characteristic, and one can
never wholly escape from the fact that the use of confidential information may be abused at times, whether intention-
ally or unintentionally.

Confidentiality is a concept associated more closely with
the medical profession than with any other outside the con-
fessional. The development in recent years of therapeutic
groups and the concept of a therapeutic community means
that the doctor–patient relationship is no longer a diadic
one; more and more it involves the patient with the whole
therapeutic team. There is an urgent need to bring the whole
concept of confidentiality up to date, but the medical profession, traditionally conservative, has shown no eagerness to
examine, much less modify, the existing practice. All too
frequently the doctors' case notes are not made freely avail-

able to nurses, social workers, occupational therapists, and local mental health personnel, all of whom have had sufficient training to understand the main content of the notes and whose training has led them to accept the importance of confidentiality. In a therapeutic community, where patients get to know more and more about each other, and patient–staff relationships are discussed with increasing freedom, problems of confidentiality come to have much less significance than they do in the formal practice of medicine. One comes to realize that even in strictly hierarchical hospital organizations, patients have a great deal of information about each other and the staff, which they share within their own peer group but which may be largely unknown to the staff. Caudill[1] has described his experience when, as a trained social anthropologist, he assumed the role of a patient for two months in a private hospital in New England. The patients discussed their interviews with doctors freely and had definite ideas about what they would reveal to their doctor and what they would keep to themselves.

Nurses trained by modern methods have come to realize that they must avoid special relationships with patients—and particularly confidential communications. They make it clear to the patient that while they are glad to listen, they cannot withhold information from the doctor and other personnel who can use it to the patient's own benefit. In much the same way, the culture of the patient's world in a therapeutic community comes to accept the fact that, where patients cannot themselves feed back important material, they may require help and encouragement from their peers to do

1. William Caudill, *The Psychiatric Hospital as a Small Society* (Cambridge, Mass., Harvard University Press, 1958).

so. What matters is that the material fed back is treated with the seriousness and skill it deserves. Clumsy or unskilled handling of such material will result in the disappearance of feedback in the same way that in a diadic treatment relationship a patient will not continue to communicate his emotional problems if he derives no ultimate benefit from such a procedure.

When a patient feels that he should feed back information about another patient for the latter's good, the other patient may be angry and threaten reprisal. Such a threat may be expressed after the group meeting. Provided the situation is fed back o the group the following day or dealt with by immediate confrontation in a living–learning situation, no harm is done. Not only is the situation kept within the group's control, but individuals in the group learn how to handle crisis situations. The extent to which feedback can be used is in part determined by the sophistication and skill of the patient group, as well as the staff. To feed back a patient's intimate confidence before he has developed any belief in the treatment itself or in the peer group, is to court disaster. The danger is more apparent than real when one patient tells about another, because patients are very understanding about their peers and seldom step outside the culture pertaining at the time. In general one finds that feedback develops much more rapidly in the patient population than it does in the staff. This is not surprising, since the major effort of the hospital is directed toward the treatment of the patient; but training the staff also entails a good deal of self-analysis, face-to-face confrontation, and, by implication, feedback. In general, it would seem that the more stability, competence, and confidance there is within a group, the greater the amount of feedback. At times of disorganization, either within the staff or patient population or within both, feedback can become severely curtailed, and rumor seems to blossom.

Rumor

Rumor is an emotionally toned communication based on false information that may have some basis in fact. Clearly, rumor breeds in situations where communication is limited or absent. It can best be offset by the revelation of the true facts. In any complex society, such as a ward or hospital, communications can never be complete; priorities have to be established. Thus, in a therapeutic group or ward meeting, a high degree of selection takes place, and only topics relating to the patients' well-being and emotional conflicts are regarded as relevant. To carry on a conversation about the weather in such a meeting would be initially seen as a defense, and the efforts of the group would be directed to uncovering what lay behind it. Difficulty in communication is clearly linked with anxiety: the individual or group is unsure of the reception a particular topic will receive and how communication of a problem will affect their image in the eyes of the community. A therapeutic community attempts to overcome some of the resistance to communication in both patient and staff population, but this in turn leads to certain hazards. To discuss problems and conflicts in a patient or staff group ideally results in a certain amount of treatment or education, or both. However, not all patients or staff have equal capacity for understanding and assimilating what goes on in the group discussion. Some may obtain emotional relief and increased understanding, while others may be made more anxious.

The purpose of the staff meeting following a therapeutic group or ward meeting is essentially to deal with these anxieties as part of a learning situation. However, a ward staff will have various members with different degrees of education and training—and different personalities. The tendency is, inevitably, for the more sophisticated staff members to discuss problems in a way that is meaningful to them. The less educated and sophisticated members may understand very little of what goes on.[2] The same is true of visitors. It has been our practice in a therapeutic community to admit visitors with some professional background to all meetings, whether therapeutic or administrative. In these meetings matters which may have been under discussion for weeks may come up for further discussion, and highly controversial material may be dealt with. An inexperienced visitor is prone to make value judgments on insufficient evidence. Unlike a permanent staff member, he has no opportunity to work through his anxieties in further group meetings and may, quite understandably, communicate his erroneous impressions to his own peer group. This constitutes a serious hazard in a therapeutic community.

Unlike the traditional hierarchical hospital organization, where confidential matters tend to be contained within strict limits, the open communication network of a therapeutic community is based on a sharing of information by large sections of the community, or even the total community. If a nurse becomes pregnant in a traditional hospital, the matter

2. Patients have their own informal reviews after a group, and the same problems of education and communication probably apply.

will be dealt with as expeditiously and quietly as possible
because of the possible damage to the image of the hospital.
In a therapeutic community such an event will, in all probability, be widely discussed among the nurses and other staff,
and probably among the patients too. To ignore such situations in an official way implies that there is something to
hide and deprives the community of a living–learning situation. The way in which this should be done will depend upon
circumstances. Discussion of the subject may be postponed
and dealt with retrospectively after the nurse has left, or it
may be preferable to accept the reality of the situation and
help the nurse to achieve a state of social adjustment within
the hospital and continue with her career. The more the
hospital culture deviates from the traditional culture, the
more it will tend to arouse resistances from the outside public
and furnish material for rumor formation. New attitudes
and new practices within a hospital are bound to lead to a
certain amount of misunderstanding and distortion in the
outside world, if only because they are unfamiliar. In such
a situation rumor may take on a negative or destructive form,
which may be society's attempt to protect itself against
change. To deal with rumors circulating about a hospital
may call for a great deal of courage and judgment on the part
of the administration: merely to conform to the expectations
of local society may be to miss an important opportunity for
educating the public. The temptation is always to avoid
publicity, particularly where the press may become involved,
but this avoidance mechanism can be invoked too frequently.
Obviously much depends upon the actual circumstances and
the sanctions from the employing authority. Any progress in
the direction of enlightened public opinion will inevitably

pass through stages of misunderstanding, rumor, and conflict, before a change in community attitudes can be achieved.
The probability is that there may be far too few creative
rebels in the medical profession and that the whole training
in medicine predisposes one to conformity, rather than to
question the status quo.

Sanctions

In a therapeutic community the problem of sanctions is
constantly under discussion. In order to foster security any
community must have definite limits as to what behavior is
unacceptable. In the prisoner-of-war camps during World
War II, the need for sanctions soon became evident. During
the early part of the war when there was a severe food shortage and no established culture at the German camps, there
were many instances of near anarchy. Men would lie, cheat,
and fight for food and other rare commodities. Out of such
chaos grew many examples of a highly sophisticated social
structure. At the end of the war a follow-up study revealed
some interesting trends.[3] Many of the men had become much
more sensitive to the needs of others and were described by
their wives as more socially conscious than before they left
home to enter the army. They had seen new possibilities in
role relationships and no longer assumed, for instance, that
the wives would look after the baby and the washing up while
they did the heavy chores. It was now much more possible for
husband and wife to discuss a project such as redecorating a
room and find a mutual satisfaction in their shared task.

Apart from violations of the law, the only ultimate sanc-

3. Adam Curle, *Human Relations, 1* (1947), 42.

tion available to a hospital society is that of dismissal. In a therapeutic community this is a particularly difficult sanction to enforce because of the need to obtain some kind of consensus from both patients and staff. It is easy enough to say that violence will not be tolerated, but there are many parameters to such a concept: violence in an excited schizophrenic is seen as very different to violence in some aggressive character disorder. The more the deviant behavior goes against the expressed values of the local community, the greater the likelihood of some definitive action. Violence, sexual assault, and drug peddling go against the mores of most subgroups within the British culture or North American; but drinking, staying out late, and stealing produce more mixed feelings in the hospital community.

Deviant behavior can be seen as a form of communication, but to elicit and understand what lies behind such behavior is a difficult and painful process. An example of the problems created by sexual behavior in the patient population illustrates many of these difficulties. First, it is almost impossible in most instances to be fully aware of what has actually happened. Secondly, patients are frequently in the hospital precisely because of lack of control, and at the same time they have a great need to feel wanted and loved. Finally, even in the most active hospital day there is plenty of time for leisure, and the modern tendency is to encourage the mixing of sexes both within the hospital and outside. When society in general is so mixed up about its values, what values can a hospital proclaim as appropriate?

Negative sanctions can be applied with comparative ease in extreme cases of violence or sexual assault, but even here facts are hard to come by. In a therapeutic community the culture may be of considerable help in this direction. The acceptance of a feedback principle by many of the staff and patients means that "informing" can be seen as a positive rather than a negative action, intended to bring help to the individual when he himself is not able to communicate. The implication is that by informing, the individual's peers or the staff are making the situation available for discussion with a view to treatment or rehabilitation. As we have said before, such action calls for considerable skill on the part of the staff and the proper sense of timing; and when possible it is better to wait until such time as the patient himself is ready to discuss the problem. Where his peers are concerned he may well feel resentful and tend to take reprisals after the meeting. If a therapeutic culture has been established and if there are the requisite psychodynamic skills in the staff and patient bodies, then an examination of deviant behavior may result in considerable understanding. Even so, such understanding may increase rather than lessen the problems created by the need to have certain limits and apply sanctions.

Take the case of an inadequate, dependent male who has grown up in a family where the father has either been absent or dominated by his wife. Under such circumstances, it is not improbable that the son will have difficulty in playing a masculine role. A patient of this kind responding to treatment in hospital may well feel encouraged to try to establish a more mature relationship with a girl than has been possible in the past. In my experience such a relationship is well tolerated in a therapeutic community and may on occasion lead to a not unsatisfactory marriage.

Staff anxiety tends to be aroused in situations where deviant behavior is carried out in such a way that it appears to be in defiance of the mores of the hospital community. In other words, we all tend to live by a double standard, but on the surface we appear to uphold the group mores. The temptation to punish behavior in others that touches on our own inner conflicts can be understood as an attempt to deny our own deviant tendencies. To ignore society's sensibilities by defiant, deviant behavior is in a sense to offer oneself up as a convenient scapegoat. Everyone feels free to project the image of themselves that they do not wish to recognize on to that of the sacrificial lamb.

A living–learning situation built around such circumstances can help to make everyone concerned more aware of themselves, and this in turn may make it very difficult for the group to apply any sanctions at all. Frequently, however, a split may appear between various factions of the population. The cleavage may be between patients and staff, the former often tending to identify with one of their peers and projecting much of their hostility onto staff authority figures. Sometimes the split is between the nurses and doctors. The lives of the nurses and their families are often intimately bound up with those of the people living in the hospital vicinity. Liberal attitudes may develop that are socially acceptable in this unique hospital setting, but similar attitudes based on understanding cannot easily be reproduced in the outside world. The result is that while a nurse may have an understanding of the situation within the therapeutic culture of the hospital, he or she may not be able to communicate this to the spouse and may have no success in modifying the attitudes of the neighbors.[4]

4. This is not to suggest that a slow process of education is not going on all the time. There is some evidence to suggest that the gap

A nurse's initial anger at defiant and deviant behavior will, under these circumstances, be reinforced by what the spouse has to say about the stories circulating in the neighborhood about the hospital and its inability to control the patients. Such stories, even if only partially true, reflect directly on the nursing staff as well as on the hospital administration. It is not surprising that under such circumstances, the nursing staff tends to favor a culture that reflects the surrounding community to a greater extent than do the doctors, who tend to be less involved locally, more hospital-centered, and identified with the concept of a therapeutic culture. A situation may easily develop in which the nurses want to apply sanctions to a deviant patient or patients and the doctors feel that to do so would be to disregard the patients' treatment needs. The doctor, under such circumstances, finds himself in a dilemma: he wants to go along with his nurses and retain the identity of the team and the principle of decision-making by consensus; at the same time he may feel, more than the nursing staff, that by applying such sanctions he would forego his responsibility as a doctor and do real harm to the patient. In a situation of this kind it is of great importance to have several competent leaders. If several leaders are present, one or more will be virtually uninvolved in the split between the doctor and the nurses. Many factors other than the central problem may be involved in the split and act as a reinforcement to the crisis situation. Change of

---

between the "experts" and the general community regarding attitudes to mental illness is tending to close. See, for instance, Paul V. Lemkau, and G. M. Crocetti, "An Urban Population's Opinion and Knowledge about Mental Illness," *American Journal of Psychiatry, 118* (1962), 692.

nursing staff, rivalry over leadership, feelings of resentment
—that too much responsibility is being delegated from the
doctor to the nurse—and so on, can all contribute to a
situation of this kind. Indeed, the danger of the patient being
made a scapegoat for such interstaff conflicts must always
be kept in mind.[5]

In a therapeutic community decision-making by consensus
is never easy, and many situations occur when no consensus
can be reached. Such instances are taken to indicate that the
community is not ready to make a particuar decision, approve
some new undertaking, or change an established pattern. In
theory one tends to postpone action until such time as consensus has been achieved. Sometimes this is quite impractical,
particularly in crisis situations, when sanctions appear to
be called for—at least in the opinion of some members. The
important thing is that a delay should not be at the cost
of the over-all feeling of security within the hospital community. Any society needs to feel that there are ultimate sanctions that will be invoked—irrevocably, if required. Without
such belief, backed up by actual demonstration, society, or
at least some of its more insecure members, would anticipate
anarchy.

There is no doubt that in the case of psychiatric hospitals,
society places the ultimate responsibility for patient treatment and behavior on the physician superintendent and the
consultant psychiatrist. Men in these positions hold a remarkable authority over the general public and (in England and
Wales) without legalistic intervention are in a position to
commit patients to hospitals—with the loss of civil rights—

5. A. H. Stanton and M. S. Schwartz, *The Mental Hospital*
(New York, Basic Books, 1954).

entirely on their own responsibility. No matter how democratic and egalitarian the social structure of a therapeutic community may be, there is never any doubt that the ultimate responsibility rests with the psychiatrist. Whether he ever uses this authority in making unilateral decisions will depend a great deal on circumstances. However, even in considering the most democratically organized hospital, one should never forget that the psychiatrist has a latent authority that he may invoke in any serious crisis situation. He should be ready to assume this responsibility if a conflict cannot be resolved and if the prolongation of the tension and uncertainty would be to the detriment of the patients, staff, or both. It is assumed that the psychiatrist's training gives him an ability to use his authority wisely, although some people might question this. Nevertheless it is hoped that the experience in a therapeutic community contributes to a greater sensitivity to the feelings and attitudes of other people and provides that, in making such a decision unilaterally in a crisis situation, the leader be at least cognizant of all the factors involved.

I doubt if it is ever really necessary for a psychiatrist to use this latent authority. Such a situation is more likely to occur in relation to public opinion than in the case of an internal conflict. A physician superintendent inevitably tends to be more informed about what the world at large is thinking and feeling about the hospital. The superintendent may feel that his colleagues and the hospital population generally are not sufficiently informed about some critical issue. Even when circumstances demand immediate action and the occasion makes it necessary to take a unilateral decision, every effort should be made to explain the reasons for the decision retrospectively. Such a discussion can well turn into a learning situation; the superintendent may realize that he acted too hastily, left important factors out of account, and so on. Equally, the hospital personnel may be confronted with some of the problems posed by the need to relate not only within the hospital but also with the community beyond. In a sense the superintendent has the function of protecting the hospital society from outside interference so all can get on with the task in hand. Hospital personnel tend to have little interest in administration and feel intolerant of the bureaucratic brakes, which, inevitably, they see as mere muddle-mindedness by the bureaucrats. The superintendent is properly the person whom they use as a scapegoat, but this can reach dangerous proportions if the hospital community is not willing to accept certain essential messages from the outside world.

Chapter 4. Social Learning

In his comprehensive study of theories of learning, Hilgard[1] suggests a provisional definition:

> Learning is the process by which an activity originates or is changed through reacting to an encountered situation provided that the characteristics of the change in activity cannot be explained on the basis of native response tendencies, maturation, or temporary states of the organization (for example, fatigue, drugs, etc.).

In simple terms, unfulfilled needs such as lack of love, the urge for dominance, curiosity, and so on motivate the individual to simple, trial-and-error explorations, which cease when an adequate behavioral response is found. This is accompanied by a feeling of need-satisfaction. Such responses are repeated until they become automatic and their repetition no longer requires explanation and effort. This situation is analagous to the feedback mechanism described

1. E. R. Hilgard, *Theories of Learning* (London, Methuen, 1958), p. 3.

in cybernetics. However, as the individual matures, ever more complicated situations arise, requiring the learning of new adequate responses. Erik Erikson[2] sees maturation in children as a series of crises leading to disorganization and then reintegration of the ego at a higher level when the crisis situation has been mastered. Learning of this kind is complicated and painful: old learned patterns, adequate in previous situations, must be unlearned because they stand in the way of acquiring new and more adequate patterns of behavior.

One can make a somewhat arbitrary distinction between teaching, or the acquisition of knowledge by a process of one-way communication, and learning as a subjective experience involving some modification of the personality and two-way communication. In this sense, teaching implies that the student is the passive recipient of information and has no opportunity to interact with the teacher with a view to exploring new parameters and possibilities relating to the subject being taught. Teaching of this kind is related to the somewhat mechanistic concepts of the older behaviorist theories.[3]

Social Learning

Social learning as practiced in a therapeutic community implies two-way communication motivated by some inner need or stress leading to the overt expression of feeling and involving cognitive processes and learning. This is closely

2. E. H. Erikson, *Childhood and Society* (New York, Norton, 1950).

3. E. L. Thorndike, *Selected Writings from a Connectionist's Psychology* (New York, Appleton, 1949).

related to the Gestalt theory of learning.[4] The term social learning describes the little understood process of change which may result from interpersonal interaction, when some conflict or crisis is analyzed in a group situation, using whatever psychodynamic skills are available.

Psychoanalysis and ego psychology have added a great deal to our knowledge of learning and the therapeutic process, which are intimately linked. Freud described thinking as a substitute for acting, that is, acting in fantasy. Tension, resulting from innate need or unresolved problems, supplies the motive driving force to resolve the situation, either by trial and error, or by some cognitive process. When a solution has been achieved, a feeling of satisfaction ensues. In this sense, the therapeutic process can be described in terms of learning theory. To quote from Alexander:[5]

During treatment the patient unlearns old patterns and learns new ones. This complex process of relearning follows the same principles as the more simple relearning processes hitherto studied by experimental psychologists. It contains cognitive elements as well as learning from actual interpersonal experiences which occur during the therapeutic interaction. These two components are intricately interwoven. They are described in psychoanalytical literature with the undefined, rather vague term "emotional insight." The word "emotional" refers to the inter-

4. W. D. Ellis, *A Short Book of Gestalt Psychology* (New York, Harcourt, Brace, 1938).
5. Franz Alexander, "The Dynamics of Psychotherapy in the Light of Learning Theory," *American Journal of Psychiatry, 120* (1963), 440.

personal experiences; the word "insight" refers to the cognitive element. The expression does not mean more than the recognition of the presence of both components. The psychological process to which the term refers is not yet spelled out in detail.

The introduction of the feeling level in interpersonal exchange introduces a crucial element in social learning. Western culture frowns on the free expression of feeling and superimposes values such as politeness, good taste, and morality, which tend to obscure the individual's subjective feelings. Conformity to the mores and expectations of society is a very powerful element in our educational and family systems. To deny to such an extent the free expression of feeling is to limit the opportunity for social learning.

It is essential that we add to the conscious aspect of feeling the concept of corrective emotional experience:[6] over a period of time emotionally charged attitudes developed in childhood have to be corrected by reliving similar situations in the immediate present. One important factor in bringing about change and learning is that the teacher—or psychoanalyst—behaves very differently in the present situation, compared with the parents in the past. As an example, the child of a dominant parent may be forced to repress his own rebellious, aggressive responses in order to avoid the parent's anger. Such timidity may persist into adult life and can only be modified when a tolerant and understanding teacher—or therapist—behaves very differently in situations in which the individual anticipates anger or rejection. In a therapeutic

6. F. Alexander and T. M. French, *Psychoanalytic Therapy: Principles and Application* (New York, Ronald Press, 1946).

community there are many opportunities in the ordinary life
of the patient—or trainee—where neurotic patterns of timidity, fear, and so on, which are derived from the past, can
be reproduced in the present and handled much more effectively in the presence of an understanding and therapeuti-
cally skilled authority figure. In brief, social learning includes
both conscious and unconscious elements, although the use
made of the latter depends largely on the training and experience of the individual teacher or therapist.

We have placed a great deal of emphasis on the expression
of feeling, which is intimately linked with concepts such as
interest and motivation. While this seems to be one of the
fundamental beliefs regarding therapeutic community practice, its importance may well have been overestimated; certainly the resistance to the expression of feeling in social
intercourse generally is one of the factors operating against
the adoption of therapeutic community principles. When
developing a new hypothesis, the temptation is always to
overemphasize what one is particularly interested in. In this
context, there is no intention to devalue the importance of
teaching as practiced in centers of education; the two aspects
of education are complementary. In the same way, we have
tended to overlook the importance of thinking as an aspect
of learning. New ideas may occur to individuals in situations
when they are quite alone and when there is no apparent
emotional element involved. Such original thought may well
be an end-product of what has here been called social
learning, but there is every reason to think of it as occurring
quite independently (although this might not be accepted
by some ego psychologists and psychoanalysts). The concept
of emotional insight propounded by psychoanalysis does not

preclude the possibility of insight resulting from the process of contemplation in a tranquil environment.

To summarize, the concept of social learning implies social interaction around some problem area. Discussion of interpersonal problems must arouse feeling, whether it is expressed overtly or covertly. Frequently individuals tend to cover up their feelings, and such tendencies are encouraged in our culture. Moreover, feelings are frequently repressed and unconscious. It may take considerable skill on the part of the leader to create a group climate in which such latent feelings may become manifest. People often lack the motivation to examine their feelings, let alone share them with others. In our competitive and insecure world it is hard to find a group climate where there is a sense of security without fear of reprisal. To achieve such a group climate requires a social structure where the sanctions are positive and there is no threat from the abuse of authority. Such a climate is difficult to achieve in a therapeutic group and even more so in staff meetings, training programs, family groups, or group situations in the community. In other words, the social milieu in which social learning can occur is as important as the skills required to analyze interpersonal interactions within the group, to uncover latent content, and to examine the various solutions to problems raised in such a group. Social learning is used to cover this set of circumstances, and the terms "living–learning situation" and "crisis situation" are used in a very arbitrary way to refer mainly to the amount of feeling inherent in the situation. When there is a moderate degree of anxiety, as occurs in most interpersonal interactions around problems of everyday living, whether in hospital or in the outside community, we use the term "living–

learning situation." Where, however, crisis occurs with accompanying severe anxiety, the term "crisis situation" is used.

In both crisis situations and living–learning situations, the term "confrontation" is used to convey the bringing together which makes social interaction, the expression of feeling, and social learning possible. The confrontation may or may not succeed in its purpose of resolving a conflict or achieving a learning situation. The outcome of the confrontation depends on the inherent skills of the participants, the motivation of the individuals concerned, and the nature and complexity of the conflict or crisis. The timing of the confrontation is of extreme importance, particularly in a crisis; if unduly delayed it may lead to disaster, and the opportunity of creating a social learning situation may be lost. Even in living–learning situations confrontation should occur at the time when the interaction is in progress. To talk about a situation retrospectively deprives it of much of its feeling tone, which seems to be an essential ingredient in social learning. It is for this reason that much of the supervision that occurs in formal training may be less effective than it would be if the supervisor were a participant in the ongoing living–learning situation or crisis. We will return to this subject when discussing staff training.

Crisis Situations

Crisis may be defined as an intolerable situation which threatens to become a disaster or calamity if certain organizational and psychological steps do not take place immediately. A crisis may lead to regression or disintegration; it may be resolved, or partially resolved; it may lead to growth and learning on the part of the participants. Crisis situations, of course, are not unique to psychiatric hospitals. They play a vital part in the development of nations, cultural groups, families, and individuals. The importance of crises and their resolution in such everyday life situations such as separation, bereavement, marriage, pregnancy, surgery, and retirement, has been clearly described by many authors. The pertinent literature has been summarized by Tyhurst and Caplan.[7]

Each crisis has a history. The series of events that precedes the crisis and the resulting role relationship of the participants form the structure in which the crisis takes place. The crisis itself produces, in exaggerated and stark relief, the subtle themes and conflicts that have slowly evolved in the preceding months. The family crisis that often precipitates the admission of an individual to a psychiatric hospital, for example, highlights the conflicts, communication blocks, and role relationships that have evolved in the past.

The psychiatric hospital in many ways provides a laboratory situation for experimentation with methods of productively resolving crisis situations. Admission to hospital and discharge from it are common examples of crises involving psychiatric patients; so is the transposition of the patient's social problem from the outside to the ward environment, with a buildup of tension until a ward crisis occurs.

7. J. S. Tyhurst, "The Role of Transition States including Disaster in Mental Illness," *Symposium on Preventive and Social Psychiatry, Walter Reed Army Institute of Research and National Research Council* (Washington, D.C., United States Government Printing Office, 1958), pp. 149–67. G. Caplan, *Principles of Preventive Psychiatry.*

The crisis situations in the psychiatric hospital differ from many of the crises described in the literature in that they often do not involve major environmental changes. They are instead produced by growing conflicts among individuals. These conflicts commonly involve the roles of the individuals concerned and often are intensified by blocks in communication among them.

Working within a therapeutic community framework, we have evolved a procedure of face-to-face confrontation for dealing with hospital crisis situations. It aims at resolution of the crisis with maximal growth and learning on the part of the patients and staff involved. This model for crisis resolution has five basic principles:

1. *Face-to-Face Confrontation* A face-to-face confrontation involving all major participants in the crisis situation is essential to its productive resolution. We are impressed with the distorted communications that regularly occur in the emotionally charged atmosphere of the crisis situation. Only by looking at the many contributing factors to the crisis from the different points of view of all the major participants, in the dispassionate setting created by strong neutral leadership, can each participant in the crisis obtain a more objective understanding of his own involvement. When major participants in the crisis are left out of the confrontation situation, the distortions produced by the other participants are not corrected.

2. *Timing* Confrontation should occur as soon as possible after the crisis, or even during the crisis—if the level of feeling is not too high. To delay confrontation to the next day, for instance, may be to lose the possibility of social

learning. By the next day the individuals concerned will have attempted to deal with their anxiety by various devices, including discussion with a supportive peer group. Various ego defenses such as displacement, projection, and rationalization will be mobilized and seriously impair the value of the confrontation.

3. *Skilled Neutral Leadership* Crisis situations evoke various ego defenses which depend on the personality of each individual, the nature of his involvement in the crisis, and, in particular, the nature of his relationships with the other people affected by the crisis. Thus the first task of those who practice social intervention with a view to social learning is to analyze the factors contributing to the crisis: to clarify its history and psychodynamics. Then the most appropriate timing for the first and succeeding confrontations (if any) must be determined. Finally, decisions must be made about who should participate. One or more participants in the actual confrontation should be skilled in group methods and have no personal involvement in the crisis situation. We have found that leaderless or poorly led confrontations are often unproductive.

4. *Open Communication* Productive resolution of a crisis situation often involves extremely painful communication about feelings among people. The setting in which the confrontation takes place must be such that these feelings can be openly expressed without fear of reprisal.

5. *Appropriate Level of Feeling* If the feeling around a crisis is too strong or too overwhelming, growth and resolution do not take place. If, on the other hand, there is not a

sufficient level of anxiety about the crisis, the participants may be insufficiently motivated for change to occur.

6. *Attitudes of Participants Conducive to Growth* The major participants in the crisis situation must be prepared to look at themselves and examine their roles, to express themselves openly, and to listen to other points of view; they must be willing to change.

Two illustrative examples of crisis and confrontation, in relation to a clinical problem and in relation to an administrative problem, may help to clarify our thesis.

A crisis arose when the door of a disturbed long-stay ward was locked for twenty-four hours. Dingleton Hospital is proud of the fact that in 1949 the physician superintendent, Dr. George Bell, initiated the first totally open psychiatric hospital in Britain. By locking the ward, the doctor in charge had broken a tradition that had lasted for eighteen years. This was done after due circumspection and proloned meetings with both patients and staff. The crisis was over the behavior of an eighteen-year-old female character disorder, Maria, who hit other patients, including old ladies, without provocation. When, following a prolonged ward meeting with all patients and staff present, the ward had failed to come up with any adequate plan to control Maria's behavior, the doctor, acting unilaterally, decided to lock the door. He made clear his belief that until the ward could assume its responsibilities for this patient, the safety of other hospital patients—particularly the elderly—should not be jeopardized. Neither did he feel that it was appropriate to deal with the situation simply by recourse to chemical restraint. This was a most disturbed ward and had fifty-six long-stay patients of both sexes.

In the daily ward meetings with patients and staff, followed by a review, the ward was able to deal with most of its problems by free communication and by using therapeutic community principles, including social learning. The next day, the crisis on the locked ward was resolved by prolonged confrontation with all the relevant patients and staff. Patients and staff among them had assumed responsibility for Maria's behavior, and when the crisis was over the ward was unlocked. However, the long-stay population in the rest of the hospital was deeply disturbed by the rumors that spread around, and it was decided to hold an immediate confrontation involving the staff of the disturbed ward, all the charge nurses, and the senior staff of the hospital, including all the doctors. This confrontation of senior staff lasted just over an hour.

In the discussion, the recent history of the ward emerged: the ward had divided into two separate groups of patients; one was seen as potentially capable of being rehabilitated to the outside world; the other was seen as having to be rehabilitated to a prolonged hospital existence. These two groups had met separately every day. The outgoing group was, hopefully, the culture carrier, assuming much responsibility for patient behavior. However, due to a multiplicity of factors, the two groups had not been working too satisfactorily, and the doctor had returned from two weeks' holiday to find the situation partly out of control. In particular, Maria was creating a crisis for the ward and the hospital as a whole. The staff decided that the two groups should meet

together, so that the whole ward could look at the situation
and try to work through the problem collectively. It developed that the patients were either unable or unwilling to
assume responsibility for Maria's behavior. It was in this
setting of frustration—for the nursing staff, doctors, and
patients—that the doctor in charge, without consulting anyone, decided to lock the door. At the combined ward meeting
the patients were more or less informed that they would have
to go on facing the reality of the situation until they finally
came up with a solution, such as a rota system to look after
Maria.

By locking the door, the doctor in charge stressed the
seriousness of his intention. It was much like locking a jury
in until such time as they could come up with their decision.
We learned that the policy worked well, and the patients had
agreed to taking turns in looking after Maria. At the same
time the staff agreed that they should contribute by sharing
responsibility for her supervision and also by prescribing
moderate doses of chlorpromazine. This action had led to
the ward being opened after twenty-four hours. The larger
crisis and confrontation meeting was in the nature of a retrospective learning situation. Although the ward members
felt that they had dealt with the crisis quite adequately from
their point of view, the hospital as a whole still expressed
considerable anxiety at what had happened. The use of drugs
on this particular ward was discussed, and participants were
told that while the nursing staff might have some patients
on tranquilizers, these were not used without some form of
group decision, even in a crisis. It seemed that the fact that
doctor had been on leave had delayed a group decision regarding Maria's behavior and the need for some chemical

restraint. The patients had felt that they were expected to
shoulder too much responsibility and were not being adequately backed up by the staff. They felt that the doctor had
been manipulated by the group into taking his aggressively
independent action as much as he had acted on his own conviction.

It seemed as though the nursing staff and patients in this
long-stay ward needed to regress to a familiar position in
the past, when the ward was run by an omnipotent doctor.
Having achieved this response the patients and nursing staff
had an enhanced feeling of potency and were able to believe
in their capacity to control Maria, which they then proceeded
to do. In a psychiatric hospital serving a discrete geographical
area, one has to live with one's failures: there is nowhere
to transfer difficult patients, nor can they be discharged easily
to the community—as happens sometimes with psychiatric
disorders in urban areas. In fact discharge sometimes is
the only sanction that one can use against character disorders
in psychiatric units serving a metropolitan area.

In this case the doctor needed to demonstrate authority by
indicating that certain limits would be set and that under no
circumstances would helpless elderly patients be subjected
to violent behavior from young character disorders. By locking the door it seemed that he was acting in concert with the
group and anticipating their needs for absolute control in
a crisis. At the same time the ward population was left with
the clear message that the doctor expected them to be able
to resolve the difficulty by mobilizing their latent resources.
This amounted to a system of reward and punishment as an
integral part of social learning. From the resulting feeling
of security, the patient morale rose, along with that of the

staff. Perhaps the most important use of this meeting was for the training of charge nurses, who had little difficulty in empathizing with the situation under discussion and participating in what was generally felt to be a valuable learning situation.

Confrontation can be usefully employed to clarify a crisis involving an administrative problem. Recently three comparatively new assistant principal nursing officers (APNO's) walked around the hospital together and observed that one of the wards was in a very untidy state. The APNO responsible for this particular ward made a comment to the charge nurse about the situation. This new APNO had relatively little awareness of the therapeutic culture of the hospital and behaved as his previous training dictated. The charge nurse was very angry because, according to the current practice on his ward, the question of untidiness would be dealt with in the daily ward meeting with all patients and staff present. In such a setting the untidiness could be looked at as a form of communication, and discussion could lead to a better understanding of the factors behind the disorder. The charge nurse referred the matter to the doctor in charge of the ward, who in turn spoke to the superintendent, and it was agreed to have a confrontation immediately, while the crisis was at its peak.

A face-to-face meeting was set up which included the three APNO's, the doctor in charge of the ward, the principal nursing officer (PNO), and the superintendent, who provided objective leadership. The group was selected to participate in this initial confrontation because of its focus on problems in nursing administration roles and clinical identification. A subsequent confrontation involved ward staff.

The first confrontation lasted almost ninety minutes. After discussing the situation relatively calmly, the ward doctor and the principal nursing officer, who, although he had been a member of the hospital staff for some time, had recently been elevated to this post, became engaged in angry exchanges. It became clear that the PNO was adopting a protective attitude toward his relatively new assistants. The tension eased somewhat when the superintendent pointed out that there was some confusion about roles and the existing culture on the ward. The APNO's, being new, were understandably eager to please the head of the nursing department. For his part, he wanted loyalty of his assistants; to a large extent they would determine his own feelings of security in his professional role. At the same time, the PNO had to identify himself with the hospital as a whole, while his assistants identified with their own particular clinical area. In both cases at least two identifications were called for, and this amounted to having two separate roles which sometimes were in conflict. The professional identity—nursing—was comparatively easy. It was used at the time of crisis because it afforded greater familiarity and comfort.

During the confrontation we examined the problems of ward identification and explored ways in which the APNO could become accepted within the ward culture and play a leadership role. The difficulties facing a new PNO were also touched on, as was his tendency to be overcautious in response to his anxiety over his new, highly responsible role. Finally, it was pointed out that the doctor in charge of the ward was too identified with his own clinical team. This was seen as one of the most progressive units in the hospital, and it produced mixed feelings of respect and envy in the rest of the hospital. However, there was a tendency for the ward to see its problems through its own particular frame of reference and be relatively insensitive to the needs of the hospital as a whole—for example, to resent the transfer of a nurse to another ward no matter how necessary this might be. There was also a tendency to devalue the work of other wards, and so on.

It was agreed that nothing should be done to interfere with the high morale and enterprizing outlook in this ward, but at the same time they had to try to become more sensitive to the over-all needs of the hospital. The meeting ended in a comparatively relaxed atmosphere, with the general feeling that there was a lot to learn by looking at the various points of view and examining one's own subjective feelings. New possibilities in terms of roles, role relationships, and the resolution of crisis situations became apparent to the various individuals.

Tyhurst,[8] in discussing transition states and crisis situations such as migration and retirement, states that

> our tendency to regard the appearance of symptoms as invariable signs of illness and therefore as indications for psychiatric treatment needs revision. It would probably be more appropriate if we regarded the transition state and its accompanying disturbance as an opportunity for growth.

The six principles of the confrontation technique already described provide one approach for active intervention at the time of the crisis or transition.

8. Tyhurst, *Role Transition States*, pp. 149–67.

Caplan[9] has added enormously to our knowledge in this field. He bases his concept of "primary prevention" in psychiatry largely on the handling of crisis situations in everyday life: "The changes may be toward reduced capacity to deal effectively with life's problems, and in that case the crisis was a harmful episode."

The lessons of war psychiatry point in the direction of immediate attention to the individual, as soon as possible after the breakdown under stress, to avoid perpetuation of symptoms. Experience with action research aimed at facilitating produtive resolution of hospital crises also suggests that effective intervention must take place at the height of the crisis.[10] We must try to view crisis situations in a new perspective. The rigid, formalized concepts of "illness" not only prevent the situation from being seen as it really is but also predetermines all roles, role relationships, and procedures under the guise of medical treatment. It seems eminently reasonable to view the concept of the trauma itself as a potential opportunity for growth; we must seek to determine appropriate procedures as a function of the interaction between the subject, significant others in his social world, and socially skilled professional workers during the period of stress. It is suggested that much greater use be made of crisis situations, whether involving patients and their families, staff, or both, to enhance social learning.

To apply the theory of social learning to psychiatric practice we need to increase our awareness of social organization as the matrix in which social learning can be practiced.

9. Caplan, *Principles of Preventive Psychiatry*, p. 36.

10. Paul Polak, "Unclean Research and Clinical Change," *Milbank Memorial Fund Quarterly, 44* (1966), 337–50.

The concept of a therapeutic community[11] stresses the importance of social structure; it underlines the need to focus on roles and role relationships and to evolve a therapeutic culture. It does not amount to a treatment methodology in its own right but complements other recognized psychotherapeutic and pharmacological treatment procedures. The social organization inherent in therapeutic community settings— both inside and outside the hospital—strongly facilitates the productive resolution of crisis situations by confrontation.

What we are now suggesting is the formation of crisis groups, when appropriate, with increased attention to timing. A crisis calls for immediate intervention if it is to be used constructively—to wait until tomorrow, or to use a later ward meeting, is to lose the momentum inherent in a living –learning situation. By the next day the individuals concerned have built up various ego defenses, and the opportunity for social learning is lost or at least diminished. We feel it is important that such situations should be utilized while the emotions are still alive and not in a retrospective way that characterizes much of psychiatric treatment, case work supervision and the psychiatrist's supervision of students.

We have found that the greatest stumbling block to the application of such an approach is the threat this approach holds for authority figures. It is very difficult for a person in authority—a doctor, a university professor, a teacher, a social worker, a senior nurse, or any trained professional—to give up the protection afforded by his professional identity. The approach advocated here demands that the professional be willing to become the subject when appropriate, and that

11. Maxwell Jones, *Social Psychiatry in the Community.*

his performance in crisis situations be subject to scrutiny. Living–learning and crisis situations are, of course, equally important with regard to people in the lower status positions. But since our culture acts against free communication of feeling, it is very difficult to get people to express their feelings without security and freedom from reprisals by those in authority.

Living–Learning Situations

This term is meant to convey the concept of social learning as it applies to problems of everyday living, the lesser problems that have proportionately less accompanying anxiety. The six basic principles outlined for crisis resolution, face-to-face confrontation, timing, skilled neutral leadership, open communication, appropriate level of feeling, and attitudes of participants conducive to growth, all apply to living–learning situations as well.

The concept of a living–learning situation may sound simple in theory, but is very difficult in practice. First there is an inherent resistance in human beings to examine and discuss what they are doing and why they are doing it. While this inertia can be found in all spheres of life where an individual is confronted by a new set of circumstances requiring or anticipating some form of response from him, here we speak of something more positive than mere acquiescence.

Social learning implies two-way communication, along with the free expression of feeling and a willingness to become involved in an examination of one's own and other people's attitudes and behavior, with a view to bringing about change and the establishment of equilibrium. A living

–learning situation implies the analysis of a current interpersonal problem and the immediate, face-to-face confrontation of all relevant personnel. Each individual is helped to
become more aware of the thinking and feeling of the
other. This leads to a more comprehensive and holistic view
of the situation as it affects every person involved. The term
as it is used here applies mainly to conscious awareness, but
it may occasionally involve increased awareness of previously
unconscious factors. Frequent exposure to situations of this
kind, if handled skillfully by the leader, can contribute to
personality growth and maturation. Everyone, including the
leader, is subject to scrutiny, and while the process may be
painful, it cannot fail to increase individual awareness, provided the group has the skill, motivation, and ego strength
to work the problem through.

A living–learning situation in the sense used here implies
a purely temporary confrontation, usually an hour's interview with the relevant personnel. Such confrontation is
relevant not only to treatment but to the in-service training
of all staff and in fact represents an important aspect of such
an educational program.

A living–learning situation, if successfully handled, will
help to avoid repetition of the conflict under similar circumstances in the future. The distinction between this and
the feedback of emotionally toned material to a regularly
constituted ward meeting or therapeutic group is an arbitrary
one. Clearly, living–learning situations occur in all group
situations. The specific use of the term implies that a face-to-
face confrontation with the personnel involved has been
brought about without delay—where there is no regularly
constituted group in which the matter could be discussed.

The very nature of such a specially constituted meeting implies a single discussion; inevitably, however, the material tends to get fed back into various regularly constituted groups and ward meetings.

An example of such a use of a living–learning situation involving both patients and staff before integration of the sexes on the wards had been introduced may illustrate what is meant. The night supervisor reported to the day charge nurse, who reported to the ward doctor, that a male and female patient, both of whom were known to be emotionally unstable and liable to form unwise relationships with the opposite sex, were spending a lot of time together. Some anxiety was expressed by the nursing staff about this relationship, and a face-to-face confrontation involving the patients concerned, the charge nurse, and the doctor was arranged by the physician superintendent. The patients were indignant about the meeting, claiming that they were being completely misunderstood by the nursing staff and that all that had happened was that they had been together in the female ward watching television. In actual fact the members of this female ward had been encouraged to invite some of the male patients to their sitting room because they were felt to be rather isolated and exclusive. The superintendent visited this ward once a week and attended the ward meetings. It was at one of these meetings that he had commented on the lack of intermingling of the sexes in the ward, and this aroused a negative reaction from both the patients and the doctor. In face-to-face confrontation it appeared that we were dealing much more with staff anxiety than with a patient's problem. The fantasies of the staff were related to their expectations of the patients' behavior—but this had no foundation in fact. The night staff was contacted and confirmed that there was no real cause for concern: the patients were never alone but were sitting together with other ward members. This situation afforded an excellent opportunity for the discussion of the differing attitudes between the physician superintendent and the doctor in charge of the ward about intermingling of the sexes. It also demonstrated the effect of staff anxiety on the climate in the ward, which brought pressure to bear on the patients to resist the introduction of male visitors into the female ward. This is partly a dependency phenomenon, because in this particular long-stay ward the patients felt extremely dependent on the doctor in charge and wished to please her. The anxiety aroused by the presence of male visitors in the ward became accentuated because of the staff split—patients being given the choice of agreeing either with the superintendent or the doctor in charge, who with the nurses anticipated indiscreet sexual behavior. This had occurred in the past with both the male and female patient in question. In a discussion of the situation it became clear that the staff was not allowing for possible growth in these two long-stay patients with limited emotional control. That they should seek out each other in view of their similar social limitations was not surprising. Both patients were stigmatized as "bad," but it was quite clear that they were having a beneficial effect on each other. The expectations of the nursing staff were modified so that they had a greater appreciation of the feelings of two patients who had been expected to give trouble, and they came to see that interaction with the opposite sex might lead to a much better adjustment, albeit a limited one.

Social Learning and Staff Training

From what has already been said it is clear that we make little or no distinction between social learning (or training) and treatment. Social learning can apply equally to social interaction among patients, staff, or both. The concept applies not only to social interaction within the hospital environment but also in the outside community. A hospital has the advantage of being a small community where it is possible to organize the social structure so that it enhances social learning. Thus it is easier to undertake the training of staff in the relatively simple social structure of the hospital or a particular treatment ward. The hospital environment also has a ready supply of trained personnel who are available at short notice to participate in crisis or living–learning situations.

The training of staff to operate in the social environment, whether in hospital or in the community, is based essentially on the use of the social factors in the environment to bring about change. Most patients come into the hospital in order to escape the stresses of the outside world, which threaten to overwhelm them, and because of some subjective feeling of confusion, inadequacy, failure, fear, depression, and so on. Treatment involves the utilization of this emotional state to bring about change so that the tension is relieved and the individual is better equipped to cope with similar situations in the future, and it is largely academic whether one calls this process treatment or learning. In order to train staff to participate in such a process of social learning, they must themselves be constantly exposed to learning situations as they occur in everyday life. The best training of this kind is probably achieved by a personal training psychoanalysis. During such a lengthy training, the subject is himself frequently in a highly disturbed emotional state, and it is again purely academic whether one calls this a training or a treatment experience. Few people have the personality strength or the finances to go through analytic training, but much can be done by the use of group methods and supervision, preferably by people who have themselves had a training analysis. This matter will be discussed further under Sensitivity Training, but it is our belief that staff members can utilize all problems as the basis for a living–learning experience.

One of the main difficulties in developing such a technique is the presence of a well-established authority structure that is characteristic of most hospitals. To take an extreme example, the head of a department may be a professor, and two-way communication may be difficult because he is unprepared to become the subject. This is not just an end result of medical education or a lust for power on the part of the individual concerned. The department expects that the professor will have the final say, particularly where teaching is concerned. The temptation to live up to these expectations is strong, and it takes a very brave man to be willing to forego the protection this omnipotent role provides him, particularly in the case of his uncertainty or ignorance.

Therapeutic communities such as Dingleton Hospital and Fort Logan Mental Health Center are criticized on the grounds that more time is spent on the training of staff than on the treatment of patients. First, it is difficult to separate training from treatment. Second, crisis situations have equal relevance to the training of so-called "ordinary" staff and to the treatment of patients who have been unable to cope with life outside. Living–learning situations have equal applicability to all levels of the administrative and treatment personnel and to patients and their relatives. It represents an important form of in-service training, particularly as many top-level administrators have had no formal training in group work and psychodynamics. One obvious difficulty is that people at this level may feel insecure and unduly threatened by the idea of entering into a situation in which their own personal performance may be subject to discussion. It takes a great deal of courage and enterprise for a medical superintendent or director of nursing to agree to enter into such a living–learning situation. It is always easy to rationalize and say that time prevents such elaborate examination of the situation. In my experience, face-to-face confrontation, skillfully handled, leads to better morale if the formal leaders are prepared to subject themselves to this kind of situation. Staff and patients at all levels come to feel that arbitrary decisions regarding their future will not be taken, and the new method allows all points of view to be brought into some kind of perspective. Even when the ultimate sanction of dismissal has to be invoked, there is a much better chance that the departing member will have none of the feeling of injustice that all too frequently is associated with a unilateral decision taken on evidence that is largely one-sided.

In both living–learning situations and staff meetings following therapeutic groups, it is very difficult to overcome the idea that by discussing staff performance one is criticizing. Criticism too often implies fault-finding and does not convey the positive gains of a learning situation. It is as though we need a new word to describe the individual's performance in an interactional scene with a view to examining it and, if possible, improving it. It requires at least a year of training before staff members are able to understand fully this process of examination with a view to learning and personality growth. Some people can never get used to such a self-examination in a public setting, no matter how skillfully this is conducted. In fact a large part of a hospital population, possibly the majority, finds this approach alien to their personalities. This fact sets a severe limitation on the possibility of developing therapeutic communities that involve all hospital personnel.

A living–learning situation may deal with some latent content, but on the whole we are concerned with examining the emotional interaction among several people at a largely conscious level. Properly handled, this will usually lead to a lessening of tension between the members and result in a clearer understanding of the conflict. At times the successful resolution of the problem means that the individuals will be more competent to handle a similar situation in future; on other occasions the situation may merely have a cathartic effect, allowing the individuals to blow off steam and thus bring about a temporary lessening of tension without much learning.

The concept of social learning implies that the teacher is himself an integral part of the learning process. Moreover, confrontation implies the formation of a group of people concerned with a particular crisis or living–learning situation. This contrasts sharply with the type of supervision associated with the training of psychiatrists in individual psychotherapy or case workers. In individual supervision of this kind the

teacher is drawing on experience, and teaching of this type
has certainly stood the test of time. However, the discussion
turns on what the trainee recalls or perceives in situations
which he discusses retrospectively. There is no way of testing the accuracy of his perception and how far the situation
is colored by his own personality and emotional difficulties.
When the supervisor is himself present in the interactional
situation, he is in a position to compare his own feelings and
impressions with that of the trainee. Supervision through a
one-way screen has the advantage of increased objective
awareness on the part of the teacher. Our preference is for
supervision in a group setting where the teacher is himself
involved in the interaction and so can participate in the
process of social learning. Such a situation makes greater
demands on the teacher, whose own performance is now
under scrutiny by the group and when appropriate may be
the subject for discussion. What has already been said about
the resistance to social learning, and particularly to the
expression of feeling, applies to the lack of enthusiasm for
this type of supervision on the part of many teachers. In a
therapeutic community, group supervision entirely replaces
individual supervision and in our opinion leads to a much
richer learning experience for all. It seems a tragedy that so
many teachers cease to be pupils and can no longer benefit
from a day-in, day-out examination of what they are doing
and why they are doing it.

Sensitivity training, or T-Group training, has much in
common with what we have already said about social learning. This approach to training of professional personnel by
involving them in a group experience over a period of days
or weeks started in 1947 at Bethel, Maine. This training

laboratory has concerned itself in particular with the processes of interpersonal relationship and influence, the dynamics of intrapersonal change, the processes of group development, and the dynamics of intergroup and community processes.

In a therapeutic community it is possible to use sensitivity training to involve all levels of staff. For example, we have weekly meetings with each of the following groups: the charge nurses, the student nurses, the activity therapists, and the activity assistants. These are unstructured groups, with trained personnel present, and no formal agenda or teaching program. People are encouraged to interact as spontaneously as possible and to express feeling. Such a situation has much in common with a patient group-treatment session. There is the same reluctance to communicate freely, the same tendency to wait for leadership from the trained senior staff, and the same fear of exposing oneself to ridicule or reprisal. One could describe this process as "learning how to learn," and much depends on the skill of the leader or leaders. This learning is a transactional process, implying two-way communication among peers, rather than depending on trained staff to do the teaching. The teacher must be willing to receive reactions as well as to give, to be taught as well as to teach.

As an example of the sensitivity training session I would like to give a brief extract from a meeting that is held with our activity assistants. Two or three trained staff members are always present at these biweekly sensitivity training groups, and one finds the usual difficulties associated with any group training situation about maintaining free communication and the expression of feelings. At one particular meeting the conversation centered on a new arrival, who was expected to start as an activity assistant in a few days. At the time we had only four activity assistants, and they were divided into two camps: one pair was characterized by a tendency to be rebellious and easily moved to anger; the other pair was quieter, more thoughtful, and, probably as a result of these characteristics, appeared more intelligent. The girls discussed their tendency to divide into the two camps and saw the significance of the new arrival who threatened to upset this delicate equilibrium. They discussed freely the need to try to integrate into one group; they all hated the idea of continued rivalry and competition for leadership. One of the activity assistants had known the new arrival for years, and it was thought that she would continue her friendship with this girl. The activity assistants were all convinced that there would be competition for the company of the newcomer and found reasons why each of them would find some cause to form a special relationship. They did this with a great deal of sensitivity, and it was clear that they were already convinced that one of them was bound to be the odd one out. Each indicated her preparedness to be in this isolated position, and it was done with a strange tenderness—as though each wanted the other to be successful. When I pointed this out, one of the activity assistants shed tears, which she angrily ignored. We then talked about how much easier it was to quarrel and have overt kinds of rivalry and hostility in ordinary living, but how much more difficult it was for them to show the gentler sides of their natures.

The activity assistants then said that they had been on much better terms in the last week or two than previously and that the rivalry between the two sets of two had largely disappeared. This being so, we discussed the possibility of avoiding the pairing off into two sets of two, and one outsider, that they clearly anticipated. They were not at all sure about this, but when it was pointed out that the hospital as a whole was run as a therapeutic community and that the group identification, which was quite common, did not necessarily threaten individual friendships, they began to cheer up. It appeared that for the first time the activity assistants understood something about the concept of the therapeutic community, particularly at a feeling level. In the review following the sensitivity training group, my colleague and I agreed that at this particular age adolescents find security in one other person of the same sex. This sort of homosexual satisfaction is a much safer relationship than one with a member of the opposite sex, which means entering the stormy seas of competition and rivalry. The activity assistants were acting out the situation that would be presented by the new arrival the following week. They were studying the dynamics of group interaction, as opposed to individual relationships. The latter had been seen as safer and more familiar at that particular age, but the possibility of a group identification seemed to have many advantages.

Social Learning Applied to Education   The current educational system as it applies in most schools, universities, and other institutions formally concerned with learning or treatment, operates against the development of living–learning situations. Revans[12] made a series of observations in classrooms of ten secondary modern schools in and around Manchester, during the school year 1962–63. The teachers

12. R. W. Revans, unpublished data.

of mathematics at these schools met several times to discuss the program and agreed that they would give similar lessons to comparable classes which would be observed with movie cameras and continuous tape recordings. Revans has not yet published his findings, but his preliminary work begins to demonstrate a relative absence of two-way communication in the classroom. It also demonstrates that children respond readily to the attitude and personality of the teacher, which to a large extent determines the possibility of social interaction within the classroom as a prelude to learning. To acquire a specific knowledge, such as that information on the workings of logarithms, can be memorized during the process of one-way communication from the teacher, the blackboard, reading, or by solitary practice. This teaching of the familiar kind is an essential part of any school curriculum and is an essential preliminary to the acquisition of knowledge required for school examinations.

In the field of medical education, McGuire[13] has studied written examinations currently used in medical schools and shows that fewer than ten per cent of the questions required anything other than the candidates' ability to recall isolated information. She concludes that in medical education the evaluation of competence is limited essentially to measurement of the ability to recall fragmentary information. In another paper she concludes: "The ability to integrate data, to analyze problems, to develop and test hypotheses, to take a medical history, to observe clinical phenomena, and to synthesize these into a logical differential diagnosis and plan

13. Christine McGuire, *Journal of Medical Education, 38* (1963), 556.

of management, are only rarely, if ever, adequately as-sayed."[14]

One would think that formal teaching of this kind would of itself be so mechanical and uninteresting that it would provide part of the motive force required for a more free interchange of ideas with the teacher and pupils. Such is indeed the fact, as has been demonstrated from the early pioneer work of educators such as Neil[15] and Lyward.[16]

Teaching and social learning are both essential ingredients of any educational system. There have always been teachers who have related freely with their pupils and have introduced a good deal of social learning into the classroom. The fact remains that our present examination system and teacher training has tended to stress teaching at the expense of social learning. The time may well be ripe for a revolution in education, when "learning how to learn," and the matura-tion of the individual will be seen as more important than the acquisition of knowledge. Elementary schools, less plagued with examinations and more interested in the indi-vidual, have a more impressive record in this direction than the centers of higher education.

An interesting experiment in developing social learning in elementary schools, cross-age teaching, is being attempted in the United States. In modern society the major responsi-bility for the development and maturation of children is in

14. Christine McGuire Masserman, *American Journal of Psy-chiatry, 121* (1964), 221.

15. A. S. Neil, *Summerhill: A Radical Approach to Education* (London, Gollancz, 1964).

16. M. Burn, *Mr. Lyward's Answer* (London, Hamish Hamilton, 1956).

the hands of parents and educators. At the same time, most children are involved from a very early age with younger or older siblings, so that from early life they are involved in cross-age relationships. In other words children have an immense impact on children and in particular older children on younger ones. Cross-age teaching makes use of this potential to train older children to act as socializing agents in their relationships with younger ones. To begin with, an older child usually has a far greater capacity to communicate with a younger child than does the adult. Commuication between youngsters and adults depends on many variables. On the whole adults tend to be seen as authority figures, and communication between child and adult will have a quality different from that among children. Nothing can replace the importance of the relationship between mother and child, or teacher and pupil, but cross-age teaching points to a possible way of making far greater use of the potential for learning when children are trained to observe and modify their attitudes toward other children.

At the Ontario School District in southern California, there are twenty-seven elementary schools and five junior high schools. Thirty-one principals and six-hundred teachers are responsible for the education of approximately 16,000 pupils in this area. Cross-age teaching began in November 1965, and at the time of my visit (May 1966) involved ten teachers and approximately three hundred children.

Of the many patterns of cross-age teaching, I shall describe only one. Supposing a class of sixth graders (age, approximately twelve) are going to engage in cross-age teaching with the fourth graders (age, approximately ten). The teacher of the sixth graders, called "olders," meets with his pupils and discusses the whole plan. They are told about their potential for teaching younger children to learn, that they can communicate more easily with the fourth graders, called "youngers." Their tendency to view the youngers with some diffidence because they are seen as nuisances, unable to play their games, and provide anything of "value" for the olders is then pointed out. This first step requires considerable skill on the part of the adult teacher. Success depends to some extent on the teacher's capacity to relate to the olders and help them to learn from the training group itself. This has much in common with the idea of sensitivity, or T-Group training, as it applies to adults.[17] By communicating freely among themselves about social problems in relation to younger pupils, the olders have the opportunity for free discussion about attitudes, prejudices, and so on. This constitutes a learning situation, with two-way communication, examination of attitudes, expression of feeling, and a growing awareness of new ways of looking at situations and understanding them. In these seminars the teacher is in a position to help the olders not only in their attitude toward the youngers but also in relation to teaching techniques: how to correct errors in an encouraging rather than a punitive way, exactly what should be aimed at in teaching such subjects as arithmetic, English, reading, and so on.

The older may teach from one to four youngers at any one time, in a session lasting no more than half an hour. In their initial stages these sessions present great difficulties for both olders and youngers. Each session is followed immediately by a review, with either olders and youngers and their respective

17. Bradford, Gibb, and Benne, *T-Group Theory*.

teachers in their own classroom, or both sets together. At one review session of a sixth grade class, the children and their teacher sat around on the floor in a circle. The atmosphere was very relaxed, as the class had now become involved in the whole concept of cross-age teaching and obviously anticipated the discussion with relish. A twelve-year-old Jimmy, who had had three youngers to teach that morning, described his difficulty with Ken, a restless ten-year-old, who would not settle to any work and just wanted to go out and play in the yard immediately outside the classroom. Ken had been observed hitting a twelve-year-old girl for no apparent reason, and pulling her jumper down in a way which embarrassed her. It appeared that Jimmy had also sought out two or three other olders as teachers, saying that he could not get on with Ken. Other olders admitted that they had no greater success with Ken. The adult teacher, sensing Jimmy's despondency at his failure, said: "Let's play a game." He said he would be Jimmy and Jimmy could be Ken, and they re-enacted the situation as Jimmy had described it. The olders joined in willingly and confronted Ken with his behavior. "Ken" said that he just wanted to have a good time and was not interested in reading. When, however, it was suggested that he would be allowed to go and play whenever he had finished the reading, his attitude changed. The olders then discussed the importance of motivation in work and the importance of rewards, provided they were kept within reason. Jimmy clearly brightened up when it became apparent that he was not the only person who had failed to teach Ken, and one of the olders commented that Ken came from an unhappy home. The olders seemed to accept that this had some bearing on Ken's unsettled behavior, but they did not discuss this matter further. When talking about Jimmy's feeling of failure, another boy described how he had felt much the same. But when it was pointed out in the review after the teaching session that he had done almost all the talking and hardly gave the youngers a chance to talk, he modified his teaching procedure and learned to listen. This had meant that instead of hating the cross-age teaching he had come to be very interested in it. The adult teacher was perfectly willing to be used as a subject for discussion, and it appeared that on occasions he made mistakes and was quite willing to let the pupils correct him.

As interest in cross-age teaching grew, a role of "observer" was developed. The observer, a former child teacher, watches an older teaching and discusses his observation in the later review. An attempt is made to distinguish among opinions, value judgments, observations, and feelings. If an observer in the session just discussed had commented that Jimmy was a lousy teacher today, this would be seen as an opinion or value judgment, and as such not highly regarded by the group. On the other hand, if the observer had said "I thought Jimmy was sympathetic toward Ken and showed it by his despondency at his failure to teach successfully," this would be seen as a sensitive response, and Jimmy would be in a good frame of mind to benefit from the discussion and learn from his experience.

Participants discussed feelings with a great deal of awareness and talked about it being at "gut level." This communication was seen as something to be valued and not scoffed at, as is frequently the case in childhood culture. Careful observation was also highly prized, as, for example, the observation that an older talked three times as much as the youngers he was teaching (actually timed by the observer, who was provided with a stopwatch). The observer tried to objectify the teaching situation and fed back observations of the child's teaching performance to the review. The child becomes aware of himself as other people see him, and it came pretty close at times to painful communication as described in this book.

Cross-age teaching is an attempt to maximize the learning potentialities in social interaction between olders and youngers, under supervision of the adult teacher. It sees problems of learning as being closely linked with communication. It implies that the social and intellectual distance between adults and school children is so great as to jeopardize learning. Finally, it sees two-way communication and the free expression of feeling as the vehicles through which learning occurs.

As an addendum to this brief description of cross-age teaching, so far approximately three hundred pupils and ten teachers are participating in this program. About ninety teachers and eight principals have attended classes on therapeutic community principles at the local university, and about fifty have attended short courses in sensitivity training lasting two or three days. The vast majority of teachers in this school district have so far avoided any contact with cross-age teaching. There is, it seems, a real danger of an idealogical split (pro and anti cross-age teaching) within the ranks of the teachers. Each of the 27 elementary schools has a weekly staff meeting, but the agenda is controlled largely by the principal and there is little attempt at two-way communication, or discussion of feelings engendered by such controversial subjects as cross-age teaching. Just as it was important

to get the sixth graders identified with cross-age teaching
before any program was instituted, so would the majority of
adult teachers be helped in a similar way. Interestingly
enough, Miss Mary Peters, the Deputy Superintendent of
Ontario School District, told me that as yet there had been
no case of a child asking to change schools because of cross-
age teaching, no teacher involved in the program wished to
withdraw, and no noninvolved teachers had left as a result
of the program. The number of complaints from parents had
not increased since the program started in November 1965,
and the evidence suggests that the parents were positively,
rather than negatively, oriented toward this new venture. A
videotape, showing the program in action, was shown to an
audience of over one hundred parents. This was considerably
more than attended the ordinary meetings of the Parent–
Teachers' Association. Discussion was animated and no
criticism was voiced. Some parents described a change in the
attitude of their children. They now found the children much
more interested in them as people and this helped them to
feel nearer to their children. At the time of my visit, nine-
teen mothers of olders were attending a course of twelve
seminars on therapeutic community principles run at the
local university. Their field work consisted in watching a part
of the cross-age teaching program once a week, but not
attending a class in which their own child was involved. Four
mothers were about to start as assistant teachers within the
program.

There are many interesting developments in education,
and primary education in Britain, seems to be particularly
lively. It is probably true that cross-age teaching is not new.
Rural schools in Scotland have used older pupils to help

out in teaching because of the shortage of adult teachers for the past century. The serious attempt to involve children in learning situations concerning relationships and social issues, however, is relatively new. To the best of my knowledge, this particular devlopment was initiated by Peggy Lippit and her coworkers in Ann Arbor, Michigan, some six years ago.[18]

This account of cross-age teaching, like the concepts of the therapeutic community and the approach to social learning outlined in this book, proposes a tentative hypothesis that awaits further proof. There are, however, striking similarities between the theoretical assumptions made in cross-age teaching and therapeutic community practice. Considerable emphasis is placed on the importance of the peer group and the culture within which it operates. The whole idea of training children in how to develop relationships has much in common with the basic training of nurses in a therapeutic community. The role relationship between nurse, patient, family members, and other staff is seen as an essential part of treatment. The idea of a functional role, as an older relating to younger pupils under supervision by the adult teacher, followed by a review session, fits in with therapeutic community principles.

18. P. Lippit and J. E. Lohman, "Cross-Age Relationships: An Educational Resource," *Children, 12* (1965), 113.

Chapter 5. The Therapeutic Community in the Community*

The concepts spelled out in the earlier chapters of this book can, in varying degrees, be applied to community psychiatry, but the circumstances are very different. A hospital community is a microcosm of society, and everyone shares a single goal, the improvement of mental health; the staff members have special training, new people are attracted to the hospital because the particular orientation appeals to them; leadership by the most highly trained and appropriate individuals follows a predictable fashion, and the social structure can largely be molded to suit the treatment goals.

The methods employed in the creation of a therapeutic community in an institution have been described elsewhere.[1] The development of an institutional therapeutic community

* With Joy Tuxford.

1. Jones, *Social Psychiatry; Social Psychiatry in the Community.* Rapoport, *Community as Doctor.* D. V. Martin, *Adventure in Psychiatry* (Oxford, Bruno Cassirer, 1962). D. H. Clark, *Administrative Therapy* (London, Tavistock Publications, 1959). Robert Rubenstein and Harold D. Lasswell, *The Sharing of Power in a*

heightens our awareness of the therapeutic potential of the wider community. The population involved is far greater; the social structure is vastly more complex; competing interests vie for leadership, and in extreme cases the business tycoon, the autocrat, or the aristocrat, may seek power for its own sake. It is difficult enough to talk about the social structure of a community, but to talk about modifying such a structure to achieve any goal such as mental health is to be beset by a sea of variables.

Over the last twenty-five years behavioral scientists, psychiatrists, and social workers have shown an increasing involvement at an operational and research level with the community.[2] Anthropologists and sociologists have begun to turn their attention from the culture of primitive peoples to present-day society; there is a proliferation of information about the family,[3] various minority groups,[4] as well as

_____

Psychiatric Hospital (New Haven & London, Yale University Press, 1966).

2. A. H. Leighton, *My Name is Legion* (New York, Basic Books, 1959). A. B. Hollingshead and F. C. Redlich, *Social Class and Mental Illness* (New York, Wiley, 1958). E. Cumming and J. Cumming, *Closed Ranks* (Cambridge, Mass., Harvard University Press, 1957).

3. E. Bott, *Family and Social Network* (London, Tavistock Publications, 1957). M. Young and P. Willmott, *Family and Kinship in East London* (London, Routledge and Kegan Paul, 1957). E. Chance, *Families in Treatment* (New York, Basic Books, 1959). N. W. Ackerman, *The Psychodynamics of Family Life* (New York, Basic Books, 1950).

4. A. K. Cohen, *Delinquent Boys: The Culture of a Gang* (London, Routledge and Kegan Paul, 1956). P. Townsend, *The Family Life of Old People* (London, Routledge and Kegan Paul, 1957).

studies of neighborhoods and communities.[5] A better understanding of these various groups will depend on improved
techniques in observation and analysis. The information now
available about the community in which we live, together
with the knowledge we have of the therapeutic potential in
each community, makes it desirable to widen the concept
of the therapeutic community to include the extra-hospital
dimension.

The current emphasis in Britain on regional development,
reorganization of local government, and integration of the
social services focuses attention upon the holistic nature of
such extramural development. It is generally accepted that
the community should be economically self-supporting and
that local government should provide facilities that we have
come to expect as necessary to society's functioning. However, the structure and function of society do not facilitate the
emergence of a therapeutic role for the citizen.

Over the past ten years the hospital has ceased to be the
only important place for the treatment of mental illness. The
trend now is, wherever possible, to maintain the mentally
sick person in the community rather than to incarcerate him
in an institution. Both in the United Kingdom and in the
United States, community mental health centers are becoming increasingly important. The attention of psychiatrists,
particularly social psychiatrists, and psychiatric social workers has been focused on the therapeutic potentials of community life. The family and the work situation are seen as hav-

5. J. Mogey, *Family and Neighbourhood* (London, Oxford
University Press, 1956). J. Spencer, *Stress and Release in an Urban
Estate* (London, Tavistock Publications, 1964). T. Morris, *The
Criminal Area* (London, Routledge and Kegan Paul, 1957).

ing increasing possibilities for the treatment of mental illness. In many cases psychiatric treatment now includes the whole family. Local anuthorities plan for the aftercare of the mentally sick in the community and are concerned with the integration of the social services and continuity of care.

Faced by the almost impossible task of trying to describe the beginnings of an attempt to create a therapeutic community in the community at large, we have no alternative but to describe in general terms what we are trying to accomplish. Despite all the difficulties, we still feel that the general principles of a therapeutic community have relevance for the development of community psychiatry practice.

Social Structure

In the last few years Dingleton Hospital has become increasingly concerned with its place in the community and the development of its services outside the institution. It is generally recognized by the staff that hospital treatment plays only a small, albeit significant, part in the care of the mentally sick. Precare[6] and aftercare[7] are equally important if the treatment of the patient and his family is to be successful.

6. Caplan, *Principles of Preventive Psychiatry*. P. Polak, "The Crisis of Admission."

7. Joy Tuxford, "Treatment as a Circular Process," unpublished monograph for King Edward Hospitals Fund, 1961. E. Goldberg, "Working in the Community: What Kind of Help do People Need?" *Social Work*, 22 (1965). P. Sainsbury, "Some Aspects of Evaluating Community Care," *British Journal of Psychiatric Social Work*, 7 (1964), 142–46. G. W. Brown, M. Bone, B. Dalison, J. K. Wing, *Social Care and Schizophrenia* (London, Oxford University Press, 1966).

Starting with the principle that structure and functions are complementary, we have attempted to improve communications between the hospital and the community. It seems appropriate to start with the role relationship between the psychiatrists and the family doctors in the area we serve. By dividing our medical staff into three county teams, each consisting of two psychiatrists, a social worker, a senior nurse, and a secretary, we have five individuals who all get to know the family doctors reasonably well—much more quickly than if the hospital as a whole was relating to the 68 family doctors in our region. Each county has developed its own way of bringing about this two-way communication. They may meet with the family doctors on a regular basis at the cottage hospital, at the psychiatric out-patient department, or in clinical conferences focusing psychiatric problems confronting the family doctor. The idea of using the family doctor's anxiety about a particular problem to bring about better understanding and social learning works best in home visits and when the family doctor comes with his own referral to an admission evaluation session in the hospital.

Family doctors are frequently resistant to the ideas of group and team work—they think these threaten the sacred "privileged communication." Family doctors are encouraged to find the time to attend family or ward groups. Here, by first-hand experience, they are most likely to understand group dynamics and the whole concept of group therapy.

Monthly case conferences are held with local officers of the Health and Welfare Departments, family doctors, and hospital staff. Clinical problems involving the hospital, the family doctors, and the local authority can thus form the basis of mutual education in a multidisciplinary setting. At a

more informal level we have set up small evening forums in
two of the local towns, where groups of family doctors,
ministers, schoolteachers, and the team from the hospital
meet one evening a month to discuss problems of living as
they effect the disciplines concerned. The discussion of general topics—ways to help bereaved relatives or alcoholics—
can lead to a greater understanding of everyone's contribution to a social problem. This may lead to a much higher level
of integrated effort.

The hospital attempts to involve the members of these
various groups in adminstrative and policy decisions regarding the hospital's care of the mentally sick. For example, the
family doctor is encouraged to think of himself as an integral
part of the extended system. His opinions about admission
policy[8] are canvassed and wherever possible incorporated
into the changing administrative procedures of the hospital
and the extended system. Informal meetings with general
practitioners and/or local government officers allow for
face-to-face confrontation and social learning.

At an administrative level we established a mental health
coordinating committee for the area we serve. This committee meets quarterly and has representation from each of
the four local authorities with whom we are administratively
connected, in addition to family doctors, the local general
hospital, and Dingleton staff. While this coordinating committee has no statutory powers and all decisions must be

8. "Dingleton Hospital and Mental Health in the Borders:
Research Project Financed by The Scottish Home and Health Department," in process. The Borders of Scotland refer to the counties
which form the border with England. This is the area that Dingleton
serves.

referred back to the parent body, it has been immensely useful in coordinating efforts and suggesting general lines of
policy. This committee has helped us to achieve a considerable degree of agreement about the possible siting of a new
general hospital as close as possible to Dingleton, about an
arrangement for sharing our psychiatric social workers with
the general medical and local authority services, and about
the coordination of geriatric services. In order to involve the
general hospital, the cottage hospitals, and the family doctors
to an even greater degree in an over-all coordinative service
for the area, a coordinating committee on health has recently been established. It is anticipated that within a comparatively short time these two committees (physical and
mental health) will be fused into one over-all coordinating
health committee.

The structured committee meeting with a formal agenda
does not lend itself to living–learning situations or confrontation, but feedback, discussion with expression of feeling, and social learning may occur. Such a committee can
periodically attempt to look at itself. Skillful leadership can
lead to minor changes in the structure of the meeting and
new outlooks for its members. In this way both structure and
function of the committee can come closer to that of the
therapeutic community.

The social structure of the particular community has
many informal ramifications. The local Association for Mental Health has begun to experiment with discussions on relevant problems in meetings open to the general public. One
of our established practices, given formal recognition by the
relevant county councils is to invite all school children to
visit Dingleton before they graduate. Such visits are given

top priority by the Dingleton staff. A tour of the hospital, in small groups, accompanied by the youngest staff members available (preferably aged sixteen to eighteen), is made, and interaction with patients in ongoing activities is encouraged. The visit ends with a seminar where two-way communication, discussion, and social learning, may take place. An exploratory visit by the teacher and an explanatory seminar at school before the visit help greatly, as does a visit by a member of the hospital staff to the school after the tour has been completed.

At an even more informal level—and completely divorced from psychiatry—we have helped to initiate a Border Forum, which sponsors meetings in the Border towns, where problems of everyday living are discussed with the general public. Problems associated with new town development, health, relationships between young and old, and so on are discussed in meetings attended by as many as 300 people. Even in large meetings of this kind, we have attempted to use the principles of the therapeutic community—two-way communication, expression of feeling, and social learning. These meetings are not concerned with education in a formal, teaching sense. They are meant to deal with everyday problems in such a way that people can be helped to see them in a new light and come to value discussion as a prelude to learning. How far such a general approach to education can lead to change of attitude within a community is a matter for speculation. Nevertheless one of our long-term goals is to make the community conscious of some of its own potential in bringing about a process of change.

By involving ourselves with social problems that are not directly related to mental disease, we run the risk of being criticized on the grounds that we are exceeding the function of psychiatry. This misses the point. Psychiatrists, social workers, or any other members of the helping disciplines can meet with the general public with a view to pooling knowledge and bringing about social learning. There would seem to be nothing but advantage in such a development. This brings us to the problem of leadership.

Leadership in the community is obviously more complex than leadership in a hospital. The various segments of the community have their own leaders, who cherish their independence and view with suspicion integration, amalgamation, coordination, or anything that robs them of their authority and power. To allow leaders to emerge, either spontaneously or by some ordinary process of election, is not enough. Some form of training for leadership is imperative if coordination of effort in a mental health or any other public endeavor is to be accomplished. It is wildly unrealistic to think that this will come about in the foreseeable future, but even now something can be done by applying therapeutic community principles to the problems of leadership in the community. By bringing leaders together from widely different fields in order to accomplish a single goal, one can create a situation where at least something can be learned about the concepts of multiple or group leadership. The skills of psychodynamically trained individuals can complement a social structure where two-way communication and discussion of feelings with a view to social learning are sanctioned. This can be done without arousing alarm in individuals who come together, provided the psychiatrist, social worker, or other member of the psychiatric team limits his contribution strictly to his area of competence and does not get seduced into making extravagant claims in fields which are not primarily his concern.

We have seen enough of this type of situation in the past years to make us feel mildly optimistic about the potential of such training methods. As an example, the Border Forum, which brings together for its leadership people from professional, industrial, and educational fields, had great difficulty in introducing the concept of two-way communication during the preliminary discussions. The idea of formal—lecture—teaching with a captive audience was a starting point because it conjured up the familiar image. But after two years, for example, the Forum limits the time allotted to any one guest speaker, no matter how well qualified, in order that the public may express its own feelings about a problem and, where possible, use this communication as a starting point for learning.

In brief, one of the long-term goals of our community psychiatry program is that the various leaders slowly come to believe in multiple leadership, so that the potential within any one organization can be complemented by the potential from other relevant organizations.

Function

One of the constantly recurring themes of this book has been that the proper social structure is a necessary prelude to optimal function. Thus in a hospital therapeutic community the skills of the psychiatrist can to a large extent be negated if the social organization of the hospital does not complement his individual skills. While the social organization of the community cannot be described with the same specificity, we feel, after five years' experience, that the relationship between the community and the mental health facility has become more definitive—with benefit to the mentally ill.

Social work has a crucial and developing part to play in this social evolution. The early social reformers of the last century were fired with enthusiasm to alleviate the suffering that arose as a result of conflict between man and his immediate environment; where this was impossible they provided what comfort and succor community resources would allow. Advances in social work over the last fifty years have included the development of social work techniques: case work, group work, and community work. At the same time specialization in the use of these techniques occurred, in work with the unemployed, the physically disabled, the backward, the criminal, and the mentally disturbed. This in turn led to a fragmentation of the social work profession. Current thinking and policy are now moving in the direction of a reintegration of social work both as a profession and as a functioning organization within the community.[9]

The task now facing social workers is to develop a social structure in the community and a method of operating within that social structure to allow for an over-all attack upon the diseases of our society. Such integration has occurred in the

9. Reports of the "Standing Conference of Organizations of Social Workers," 1963–66. *Social Work in the Community;* Her Majesty's Stationery Office, Cmnd. 3065 (October 1966). Evidence to the Committee on Local Authority and Allied Personal Social Services (Seebohm). B. Kent, "What's Wrong with the Social Work Services?" *Case Conference, 13* (1967), 375–78.

practice of social work with the mentally ill in the Border Communities. We were able to convince the local authorities that a psychiatric social worker employed by them would form an invaluable bridge between the hospital and the community mental health and social services. This resulted in a much greater coordination of effort in the mental health field. With the growing awareness of the importance of psychiatric social workers and the coordination of effort resulting from the social structure as discussed above, it became apparent that the division of our four psychiatric social workers into hospital and community social workers served little purpose. As the machinery of local authority inevitably moves slowly, we made an offer at a quarterly meeting of the mental health coordinating committee and indicated our willingness to share our psychiatric social workers with the local authorities on a joint-user basis. This came before any formal agreement with the local authority about details such as payment, but it meant that at the functional level we were attempting a close liaison between the local authority and the hospital service.

The psychiatric social workers have begun to identify themselves with community as well as hospital needs. Family doctors and local authority personnel now contact the social worker directly, and the psychiatric consultant is only used when it seems appropriate. Even when community problems require the presence of a psychiatrist, he is not necessarily seen as the leader of the team, and the tendency is to see the social worker as the leader in most extramural activity, although this may vary considerably according to circumstance. Of course the roles of the psychiatrist and the psychiatric

social worker—and their relationships—come up for frequent discussion. Here we see that multiple leadership is a
valuable concept for community psychiatry. "Experts" from
various fields can coordinate their efforts to relieve some
difficult situation without any particular reference to the
question of formal leadership. The danger in any hierarchy
is that it can easily become structurally encapsulated and
isolated from the population it serves. The social structure
of the therapeutic community, with feedback, living–learning
situations, and multiple leadership in a multidisciplinary
setting militates against the dangers of the encapsulated
hierarchy.

How far community psychiatry should concern itself
with matters of education is an open question. Psychiatry
must be deeply concerned with bringing about appropriate
community attitudes toward the problems of mental health.
It is notoriously difficult to break down prejudices regarding
the "lunatic." The first and most important step in this
direction is involvement in the schools. We have found that
visits to the hospital are of immense benefit in changing the
misconceptions that young people often receive from the
attitudes of their parents and the culture as a whole. A discussion after such a visit brings to light the surprise with
which most pupils react to the discrepancy between the
fantasy and the reality of psychiatric hospitals. They wonder
where the "loonies" are; are we playing straight and not
hiding the really difficult cases, and so on? In general, it
seems that education can occur within the type of structure
and function that we have described. There is no real danger
in such community infiltration and coordination, provided

that the psychiatrist does not go beyond his area of competence and the principles of multiple leadership are kept in mind.

This leads us to the topic of prevention, or what Caplan[10] has called primary prevention. Community psychiatry has much to learn about the possibilities of early intervention. One of the major stumbling blocks to early involvement is the established role of the psychiatrist. He is seen as a consultant who is approached usually through the family doctor at a point where another opinion is needed. It is obvious that the usual medical model of consultation in extreme or unusual cases is about as far from prevention as one can get.

De Smit[11] described his attempt to help people in difficulty without having to function in the formal role of a psychiatrist. He felt that it was desirable for people to be able to seek and receive help without having to "become ill." From his experience in the mental hygiene clinic at the University of Michigan, he criticizes the centripetal function of the clinic, which is available at all times for the adjustment problems of the student community. He favors a more centrifugal type of planning that allows the psychiatrist to act as a consultant to the various student counselors, so that only those cases suitable for treatment would reach the clinic. By this method the student could be seen when he is still a "person," and not yet a "patient." The role of the psychiatric social worker is much better suited to this early

10. Caplan, *Principles of Preventive Psychiatry*.

11. B. N. W. De Smit, *From Person into Patient* (The Hague, Mouton, 1963).

involvement, before the individual has had to become ill in order to see a psychiatrist.

Many individuals faced by a growing feeling of failure turn to whatever help is available in their immediate environment. Given a capacity to form adequate relationships, most people can expect interest and understanding from a spouse, parent, friend, minister, or family doctor. How much preventive psychiatry goes on at this level is little understood, but it probably represents a far more significant factor in mental health than all the formal efforts of psychiatry put together. Unfortunately the very people who most need help are those who cannot easily form relationships and are as a result isolated and alienated from society. They often draw attention to their condition by behavior that offends a society of which they are not an integral part. This frequently results in the exertion of social pressure, which results in admission to a psychiatric hospital. In such cases primary prevention, if it were to mean anything, would probably be focused on earliest childhood and the individual's inability to form social relationships in the crucial first years of life.

Help from the social environment at times of stress may prove to be the major determinant of "sickness" and "health." The housewife, feeling unfulfilled in her role as mother, may envy her husband who comes home every evening from an interesting day, with many social contacts and a feeling of accomplishment. The wife may attempt to reassure herself by talking about her day, the difficulties with the children, the unpleasantness of the shopkeepers, the malicious gossip at the neighbors, and so on. If the husband devalues her communications and compares them unfavorably with his, the wife's poor opinion of herself is reinforced. She may see

no solution but to become ill in order that her need for help can be recognized and she can at least have the concern of the family doctor or the hospital.

Regression to the helpless role of the patient in such circumstances is eminently understandable. How far primary prevention can operate in such a context is as yet insufficiently understood. It would seem reasonable to suppose that the skills of the psychiatric profession generally are needed in the handling of such situations, but whether this should be through the training and/or treatment of the spouse in order that he can relate in a therapeutic way toward the potentially ill partner, or by direct substitution therapy, where the social worker or psychiatrist relates directly to the potential patient, is still insufficiently understood. Obviously much will depend on the prevailing circumstances. What is lacking at the moment is a capacity on the part of all people concerned with mental health to make adequate assessments of the liabilities and assets in any one family situation and to follow this by an appropriate social prescription. Social assessment, followed by social prescription, brings us to the question of training.

The psychiatric hospital run as a therapeutic community has a social organization that makes maximal provision for communication, expression of feeling, and discussion with a view to social learning. In our opinion, training should, whenever practical, be based on a multidisciplinary experience. This is typified by the review following a ward meeting or group confrontation following a crisis, or the establishment of a living–learning situation.

Ultimately, we may see the undergraduate in the various disciplines concerned with psychiatry, medicine, social work, occupational therapy, and nursing, being exposed to the theories and practice of group dynamics, sociology, social relationships, and social organization. In the meantime, such theory and practice is being applied increasingly to postgraduate education, aided by such specialized training as a personal psychoanalysis, a postgraduate course in community psychiatry at one of at least eight universities in the United States, or a combined training in two disciplines, say, psychiatry and anthropology. The point of view of this book is that training in relationship therapy, group work, and so on is best carried out by using here-and-now situations, as they occur in the lives of patients, or potential patients, and their families. By involving staff in such situations, the treatment of the patient and the training of the staff overlap; the term "social learning" describes this process. This is a form of group supervision which involves the teachers from the various disciplines in examining not only other people but also themselves. Such a procedure has many advantages over the more usual retrospective supervision which allows the teacher to "play God" and excludes him in part from social learning. As community psychiatry develops in experience and skill, it may be possible to do more and more of the training outside the hospital.

In the meantime, training in therapeutic community principles is probably best carried out in a hospital that is attempting an increased community involvement.

One of the major stumbling blocks to progress in community psychiatry is the parochialism of the various professions concerned. Each discipline seems to think of the total situation in terms of its own needs. The whole situation is now being reviewed in Great Britain on a national scale. To date the emphasis seems to be on the needs of each of the professional groups, and there seems to be little awareness of the importance of the concept of multiple leadership in a multidisciplinary setting. Our hope is that the social structure can be based on community involvement and not be decided solely by committees and "experts," who have themselves long since left the field of practical endeavor.

Chapter 6. The Future

Psychiatry has in my opinion paid far too much attention to the model created by general medicine. This is inevitable so long as doctors, nurses, and other professionals associated with psychiatry take their undergraduate training in general hospitals, whose social organization is geared more to the needs of surgery than of psychiatry. The omnipotence of the medical leader, the absence of two-way communication, and the rigidly defined status differentiation, which often excludes the patient as a person, are only a few of the extreme characteristics of this setting. With such early conditioning a doctor or nurse cannot be expected to have a highly developed and sensitive social awareness; and in fact this training is highly unsuitable for the preparation of the future psychiatric doctor or nurse. People educated in this setting are not unsuitable for further training in social psychiatry, but at the very least they must face a very painful transition to the more patient-centered therapeutic community.[1] It seems

1. Maxwell Jones and Robert Rapoport, "The Absorption of New Doctors into a Therapeutic Community" in Greenblatt, Levinson, and Williams, eds., *The Patient and the Mental Hospital.*

reasonable to suggest that either the undergraduate medical experience should become more "humanized," or disciplines such as social work and social psychology, with their more appropriate undergraduate training, should play an increasingly important part in social psychiatry. Alternatively a new role with a training that is specifically structured to meet the needs of community psychiatry may emerge. How much of a doctor's or nurse's training in general medicine is valuable to the ultimate practice of social psychiatry?

Social or community psychiatry is usually practiced extramurally and calls for a reexamination of roles, role relationships, and culture of the treatment team. Can the psychiatrist survive in this extramural setting? His right to leadership in a multidisciplinary team is already being questioned, and even in the therapeutic community of the hospital he may have a social worker or psychologist as team leader.

Medical training is embedded in the concept of "illness"; the role of the patient is to be "sick." The doctor and his team are inevitably cast in the roles of healers. In our civilization "to become sick" is acceptable in the physical sense, but less so in the psychiatric sense, unless there are demonstrable symptoms such as "fits," gross psychotic behavior, and so on. Often the "sickness" is established by society itself, with deviant or troublesome members segregated in a mental hospital. In the lowest levels of socioeconomic structure we find the "bums," chronic alcoholics, or social outcasts who are not seen as serious medical or psychiatric problems at all. It is left to the courts or a few dedicated religious and social organizations to render what help they can to these individuals who are outside any psychiatric program. Psychiatry has not made any significant contribution to the treatment of sociopaths. It is difficult to avoid the impression that a moral prejudice exists toward these individuals.[2] In this connection it has been said that the psychiatrist "talks the language of the scientific method and has a professional need to consider his social preference as having resulted from scientific observation. He is in danger of replacing the semantics of social morality with that of psychological morality without changing the substance."[3] It is well known that few psychiatrists have much sympathy or interest in the problems of the sociopath, and leadership in this field in the United States comes from the social psychologist, social worker, sociologist, and criminologist.

Many more examples could be given of the arbitrary division between social and psychiatric interests and responsibilities. The clinical psychiatrist may feel that his interest should be limited to the patient. Certainly this has been true in the past. Social psychiatry is attempting to change this emphasis, but it is far from clear how far psychiatrists are willing to go. Their present training fits them for dealing with "illness." How much they can cooperate with other disciplines and deal with ordinary people in the outside community remains to be seen. The fact is that as yet little or no specific training for work in the outside community is given to the psychiatrist in training. Two of the more sophisticated centers for the teaching of social and community psychiatry in the United States, Fort Logan Mental Health Center and San Mateo County Hospital, have started a three-

2. Maxwell Jones, "Society and the Sociopath," *American Journal of Psychiatry,* 119 (1962), 410–14.
3. L. Z. Freedman, P. H. Hoch, and J. Zubin, *Psychiatry and the Law* (New York, Grune and Stratton, 1955).

year residency training program. Several medical schools, including Columbia, Yale, and the Universities of New Mexico and California, have adopted catchment areas. This will mean that the resident in training will have an increasing opportunity to be involved in the practice of psychiatry in the community outside the hospital.

Many social psychiatrists feel that our isolation from other disciplines such as education, the behavioral sciences, technology, theology, philosophy, architecture, and so on is inexcusable. Nevertheless national and international psychiatric meetings continue to be essentially unidisciplinary.[4] In this context the term social psychiatry is misleading. We need a term that implies a multidisciplinary approach to social problems, to foster primary prevention and develop an entirely new frame of reference for dealing with the whole spectrum of mental health and mental illness. Such fundamental changes will be necessary if psychiatry is to play a useful part in the new social order created by modern technology.

Vast changes in the theory and practice of education are imminent, and no one can conceptualize with any accuracy

4. The newly formed International Association for Social Psychiatry which met in London in August 1964 under the chairmanship of Joshua Bierer had a truly multidisciplinary character. Since then the chairmanship has been held by myself and the name of the organization changed to Social Psychiatry (International Multidisciplinary Federation), in an attempt to widen the concept to include much more than clinical psychiatry. This organization has been successful in encouraging the formation of national associations of a multidisciplinary character. At present we know of social psychiatry associations in Argentina, Czechoslovakia, Finland, France, Israel, Peru, Tunis, and Turkey.

what will emerge in the next few decades. The present methods of teaching in schools and colleges, static for the last thirty years, reflect society's attempt to produce a standard product to meet its functional needs. "Mass education is a child of the mechanical age. It grew up along with the production line. It reached maturity just at the historical moment when western civilization had attained its final extreme of fragmentation and specialization, and had mastered the linear technique of stamping out products in the mass."[5] The distinction between teaching as one-way communication between teacher and pupil, and learning as a social process with two-way communication, has been discussed. Teaching and learning are both important, and both must change rapidly as a result of new concepts of teaching in a computer age (programmed instruction), while learning as a social process calls for much more involvement on the part of the instructor than has been usual up to the present.[6]

Teaching as we know it today will inevitably be changed as subject matter is adapted to programmed instruction. This mechanized approach allows the pupil to learn at his own pace and involves the student in a kind of dialogue that lets him respond at frequent intervals. We are only at the threshold of these new developments, but it is anticipated that most school subjects will be learned more rapidly and effectively when new equipment is created that affords a responsive environment for the pupil. In this new era teaching by a mechanical process will produce a degree of involvement in

5. Marshall McLuhan and G. B. Leonard, "The Future of Education: The Class of 1989," *Look* (Feb. 21, 1967), pp. 23–25.
6. M. McLuhan and Q. Fiore, *The Medium is the Massage* (New York, Bantam Books, 1967).

the pupil at present largely lacking in the teacher–pupil role relationship.

The teacher of the future, relieved of much of the present demand for mass instruction, will be free to interact with his students to an extent hitherto undreamed of. Cross-age teaching is an example of the much greater teacher–pupil interaction and emotional involvement that is already emerging.

These developments in the field of education link with the central theme of this book, the concept of social learning. We have stressed that social learning involves not only two-way communication but also the expression of feeling and the presence of a skilled instructor.

Communication is developing so rapidly that national boundaries no longer isolate people; television makes it theoretically possible for the whole world to be tuned into the same program at the same time. The challenge for survival in the atomic age is linked with man's capacity to think and act globally, rather than nationally. The "teach-ins" represent an early attempt at social learning. They substitute two-way communication, and analysis of the interaction by a competent chairman, for the more competitive form of debate, where each party tries to defend and establish its position.

One of the most interesting concepts in this area is T-Group training,[7] but even this relatively simple interactional procedure, carried out by selected individuals in a laboratory setting under skilled supervision, raises many unsolved problems. A T-Group usually lasts for one or two

7. Bradford, Gibb, and Benne, *T-Group Theory and Laboratory Method*. See also Chapter 4.

weeks and begins with the withdrawal of expected leadership, agenda, power, and status. "These factors are with-
drawn less to teach the persons how to deal with stress and
more to communicate that the educator really means it when
he says that their re-education is going to be their responsibility."[8] Assuming that T-Group training does contribute
to greater self-awareness, self-acceptance, and interpersonal
competence within the group, how far can this experience
carry over from the laboratory to the world outside? Argyris
feels that a change may not be manifest in the outside world
in the same form as within the laboratory. As a result of their
experience, however, participants may become better listen-
ers, more patient, and more realistic in their home setting.
Having raised doubts about the effectiveness of the laboratory experience in changing the individual's performance
after leaving the group, Argyris goes on to explore many of
the basic assumptions associated with T-Group training:
the value of enabling a person to experience his world more
freely; that human events experienced primarily in a cognitive manner are incomplete, and the development of feelings
allows experience to be felt and integrated into the self;
that the unconscious plays a crucial role in learning and
emotional development. While he believes that there is general agreement that the emotional dimensions have been too
frequently suppressed where they are relevant to competent
learning, he doubts if all growing experiences must be
emotionally felt. Even if this is so, he asks how strong the
feelings need to be. I have dwelt on T-Group training to

8. Chris Argyris, *Explorations and Issues in Laboratory Education* (Washington, D.C., National Training Laboratories, National
Education Association, 1966).

highlight the difficulties facing this field. If under the highly specialized but relatively simple and circumscribed conditions of laboratory education, there is as yet much uncertainty about many of the basic assumptions, how ready are we to apply these principles of learning to the ordinary world?

What will be the role relationship between the psychiatrist and the educator in the future? This is an impossible question to answer because the situation is in a state of flux as at present. Even the role of the psychiatrist cannot strictly be defined because he assumes so many different roles at present and may be called upon to take on new ones in the future. From the functional point of view, one might describe the three approaches to psychiatry: psychoanalytic, empirical, and social.

1. *The Psychoanalytic*   The psychoanalyst treats a small number of selected patients, amounting to as few as a hundred in his lifetime. Many aspects of this technique are being questioned by psychoanalysts themselves, and how long this approach will maintain its dominant position, particularly in the United States, is an open question. However, few people would doubt its value as a research tool in exploring the significance of infantile life and its effect on personality development. Whether psychoanalytic training will remain as one of the cornerstones of training for psychiatrists also seems problematic. The present trend in training seems to be away from too much specialization, and on practical grounds the psychoanalytic approach is not comprehensive enough to have much value for the treatment of psychiatric problems in general.

2. *The Empirical*   The huge number of patients, partic-

ularly in state hospitals, makes individual treatment, even on modified psychoanalytic lines, quite impractical. The pressures are enormous, and the psychiatrist with a hundred or more patients at one time tends to use largely empirical methods. These methods mainly take the form of tranquilizers, antidepressants, and electroshock therapy, which, while having profound effects on many patients, operate in a way that is not fully understood. Apart from the specific effects of these treatments, they are frequently used as forms of chemical or psysiological restraint to quiet disturbed patients. The future of this approach to psychiatry is again difficult to predict. Much will depend on a more exact knowledge of the etiology of schizophrenia and other mental states and the successes achieved by social psychiatry.

3. *The Social*   Because of the newness of this approach to psychiatry, there is as yet no standard definition. The terms "social psychiatry" and "community psychiatry" frequently tend to be interchangeable and are used indiscriminately.[9] For my part, I would prefer to limit the term "community psychiatry" to the practice of psychiatry outside formal psychiatric organizations, such as hospitals, day hospitals, etc. "Social psychiatry" seems to be a generic term that includes all the social, psychological, anthropological, educational, theological, philosophical, and research factors that may modify psychiatric practice and society in the direction of increased mental health. This rough attempt to separate out categories in psychiatry will satisfy no one. There are endless

9. *Concepts of Community Psychiatry* (Washington, D.C., Department of Health, Education and Welfare, United States Public Health Service, 1965).

variations, combinations, and separations within psychiatry at the present time.

My concern here is with the role of the community psychiatrist in the future. One aspect of change is apparent in the new treatment philosophy and social organization to be found in some of the state hospitals and medical schools. Boston State Hospital is a good example of this transition. It had for fifteen years a superintendent who believed in analytically oriented individual and group psychotherapy, and developed a residency training program that was highly regarded in psychiatry. In April 1963, a change of leadership occurred and the new superintendent favored an emphasis on social psychiatry and research, rather than on psychoanalysis. Kotin and Sharaf[10] give an interesting account of the effect that the change in leadership had on the hospital as a whole, and particularly on the psychiatrists and residents in training. Writing of the changes instituted by the new superintendent, they point out that these did not consist simply of a number of new patterns to be grafted on to existing ones:

> rather, along with the programs, and reinforced by them, he attempted to effect a series of changes in orientation and role definition, involving a number of professional groups. For example, the core of the psychiatric resident's role had been concerned with learning psychodynamics and psychotherapy. One resultant problem was that such a role definition tended to train residents out of the state hospital system since the practice of psychotherapy could

10. J. Kotin and M. R. Sharaf, "Inter-Staff controversy at a State Mental Hospital: An Analysis of Ideological Issues," *Psychiatry*, 30 (1967), 16–29.

more fruitfully be pursued with middle-class, non-psy-
chotic patients, in private practice and outpatient clinics.
Dr. Lattimore's overriding conceptions were more closely
geared to the emotional problems of lower-class persons
in general, and to the needs of great numbers of state
hospital patients in particular. This particular thrust meant
an expansion of what the Resident learned during his
training years and an attempted alteration in his aspirations
for the future. In short, a change in his role as Resident and
in the role models he had chosen for his professional life.
It also implied changes in the role of senior staff members
since they would be required to teach an expanded psychiatry with more emphasis on social and community concepts and techniques. Finally, the logic of this approach
carried with it an upgrading in the status of non-medical
hospital personnel and an extension of their activities.

Boston State Hospital is symptomatic of many psychiatric
hospitals. The general feeling of dissatisfaction with present
psychiatric practice means a willingness to examine new
roles, role relationships, and social systems generally. One
major difficulty is the absence of senior psychiatrists adequately equipped to function as community psychiatrists.
There is bound to be a long transition period during which
psychiatrists can attempt to reorient themselves in the practice of psychiatry in the community. The advent of new
leaders, trained not only in psychodynamics and empirical
methods of treatment, but also in social learning and social
organization, will hopefully lead to the reevaluation of the
whole concept of the psychiatric hospital and the role of the
psychiatrist.

The social structure and function of the psychiatric hospital need to be examined critically. There seems to be no very good reason why so many of the attributes of the general hospital have been copied in the psychiatric hospital. Indeed, the word "hospital" with its implication of sickness, passive–dependent patients, and loss of individuality is inappropriate for psychiatric practice. The old term "asylum," dissociated from the stigma applied by a society fearful of mental illness, is in fact more appropriate. People who are unable to cope with the stress of ordinary life should be allowed to find asylum of a temporary kind, where with understanding, support, and psychotherapeutic treatment they may be rehabilitated back to the world outside. For patients who cannot ever expect to cope in the outside world with a society as at present constituted, or for patients who are liable to have a protracted stay in hospital, the whole concept of the hospital should be changed to something more akin to a village settlement. In such a setting, the rehabilitation goal would be to afford the individual the optimal role compatible with his disability, personality, and assets. More emphasis would be placed on the potential functional skills of the individual patients than at present. The examination of the role of the patient under these projected conditions would almost certainly lead to the disappearance of the term "patient" and also of the present concept of the role relationship between patient, psychiatrist, nurse, and so on. Indeed it is interesting to speculate how these roles would change and, indeed, if they would survive at all. In my opinion, much would depend on the nature of the developments in social psychiatry and, in particular, on the change in training of psychiatrists and nurses along the lines discussed.

The present trend of psychiatry is toward highlighting the importance of involvement in the community at the earliest possible stage, with a view to preventing the onset of "ill-ness."[11] In fact we have little or no experience or skill in the field of preventive psychiatry and as yet no methodology. The emergence of such a methodology will depend on many factors, one of the most important being the psychiatrist's capacity to relate to and understand the way of life of ordinary people in the community. This point has been stressed time and again in this book, and I make no apology for such repetition. Many people feel that the present practice of psychiatry tends to alienate psychiatric personnel from the ordinary people they attempt to serve. Unless psychiatric institutions in which the practice and teaching of psychiatry are carried out can become more humane social organizations, there is little hope that the profession will be able to do any good for the public at large. There may be some excuse for the state hospitals, handicapped as they are by shortage of staff, inept administration, and ignorant political interference, but in my experience medical schools are little better in this respect.

Problems of communication, leadership, decision-making, social learning, and so on are given little if any place in practice or training. Psychiatrists tend to remain self-centered and incredibly insensitive to the feelings of junior staff or, even worse, of patients. The capacity to listen to anything outside the psychiatrist's particular field of interest seems to have been lost in training. Above all, the capacity to form comfortable relationships, with the free expression of feeling and two-way communication with a view to learning, is a rare phenomenon. Luckily there seem to be signs of growing

11. Caplan, *Principles of Preventive Psychiatry.*

dissatisfaction, not only in psychiatry and medicine generally, but in the whole field of education. Not only are residents beginning to demand more freedom from the abuse of authority by their seniors and a larger share in policy making and modification of their training programs, but students everywhere are rebelling against the strictures of an out-dated educational system.

How far are our leaders in the educational field, whether in psychiatry or in education generally, prepared to listen and learn from interaction with the people around them? What priority is given to learning as opposed to teaching? Early in this chapter I quoted from some of the exciting vistas of future developments, as described by McLuhan. While I re-spond very positively to McLuhan's ideas, I cannot help wondering how far he has taken account of the resistance of human beings to self-examination in the presence of their peers, no matter how skillfully this may be carried out. In our present culture, acceptable social behavior demands not the free expression of feeling, but the opposite. Cultural con-cepts such as politeness imply sensitivity to other people and a capacity to reinforce their own positive image of them-selves, but exclude painful communication. In our middle-class culture, the expression of anger is frowned upon and viewed as a loss of control. Feelings that enhance the positive image of the individual or group are approved of, but criticism has a negative connotation. It is extremely difficult to get ordinary people such as nurses in training to under-stand that to discuss their performance can be a positive act aimed at increasing self-awareness and social competence.

Psychoanalysts encourage the expression of feeling by their patients but go to great lengths to avoid being involved

in such situations themselves. The patient may express negative or hostile feelings toward the analyst, who remains de-
tached and impersonal. This idea of social distance has led
to a great deal of confusion in the field of general psychiatry
and is linked with the idea of the doctor–patient relationship
and the implied status difference. Psychiatrists who may be
quite warm human beings in their ordinary lives tend to
confuse patients (and their families) by adhering to this
principle of social distance in the professional setting.
Luckily, some "untrained" nurses, particularly in geriatric
wards, have never even heard of social distance and do not
hesitate to get involved in warm interpersonal relationships
with patients and their relatives. It is easy to oversimplify the
situation, and any experienced psychiatrist knows that inex-
pert involvement can lead to serious problems and may result in a nontherapeutic relationship. What is needed is much
more emphasis on the relationships at all levels of staff and
with patients, and the way in which these relationships
should be developed.

   In discussing social learning, I have stressed not only the
difficulty in expressing feeling, which frequently represents
painful communication, but also the importance of a person
sufficiently skilled and uninvolved to be able to analyze what
happens in the interaction in a living–learning situation. It
is unreasonable to expect people to communicate feelings
and expose their intimate selves unless they benefit from
such a painful experience. We need to study carefully the
feelings and needs of many patients in the hospital who
find themselves forced into attending a daily ward meeting.
The same argument applies to staff meetings. In our experience at Dingleton, such a procedure not only alarms many

patients but also tends to antagonize their relatives and family doctors. Even if some patients do benefit from this two-way communication with the expression of feeling, they may find it impossible to carry over this approach to their ordinary life. The therapeutic culture in a psychiatric hospital may, and probably must, differ to some extent from the culture of the community outside, but to deviate too far is to court disaster. What we are hoping to achieve is some sort of equilibration between the cultures in the hospital and in the community. At the same time, by encouraging doctors and relatives to participate in group work and social learning situations, we may through time effect a change in the willingness of people to communicate more freely in their ordinary lives.

For example, in monthly meetings with small groups of ministers and teachers, we have found that there is a general reluctance on the part of professionals to confront a recently bereaved individual with a view to communication of feelings. This might well be seen as an aspect of preventive psychiatry, but so far our experience shows that the tendency is for the professional on the spot to rationalize his involvement and play for time. This may illustrate the good sense of the family doctor, or minister, who feels unwilling to encourage discussion of a painful topic if he feels incompetent to do so, and is probably preferable to producing feelings in a situation where such painful communication may not lead to social learning. On the other hand, there seems every reason to think that, at least in the case of some professionals, help from the psychiatrist may result in greater competence and confidence in handling living–learning situations as they occur.

The psychiatric institution represents a microcosm of society and has a much simpler social matrix than communities within the general population. The attitude adopted in this book is that the principles of a therapeutic community may have relevance in both the intramural and extramural dimensions, but this point of view is open to question.[12] Psychiatrists, nurses, and family doctors have in the past been trained largely or exclusively in hospitals, and it seems obvious that the social dimension (social organization, social interaction, leadership, decision-making, etc.) should be given a more prominent part in training. It is for the future to decide how far the training for social psychiatry in both the intra-and extramural dimensions can be integrated.

We need to know far more about the whole process of learning, and it would seem that in the future psychiatrists may well tend to integrate more closely not only with behavioral scientists,[13] but also with the educationalists.[14] This seems to be one of the most exciting possibilities for the future of psychiatry. It seems to me that much treatment in psychiatry could just as well be called social learning. For this trend to develop there will have to be vast changes in the training and the orientation of psychiatrists and a much greater sensitivity on their part to the feelings of the people whom they are attempting to help.

12. Maxwell Jones, "Therapeutic Community Principles within the Hospital and in the Outside Community," read at the Seventh International Congress of Psychotherapy, Wiesbaden, Germany, August 1967.

13. M. K. Opler, *Culture and Social Psychiatry* (New York, Atherton Press, 1967).

14. J. S. Bruner, *Toward a Theory of Instruction* (Cambridge, Mass., Harvard University Press, 1966).

If social psychiatry is to accomplish anything, then it will be as a result of an increased capacity to utilize the latent forces within society itself. My hope is that psychiatry can survive in this field by playing a modest but important role, along with the behavioral scientists, educationalists, and, above all, the people most intimately concerned—patients, their relatives, and society at large.

Index